HELP WITH AN

150 EASY TO READ TIPS TO COPE WITH AND OVERCOME ANXIETY, WORRY & PANIC

GED JENKINS-OMAR

First published 2020 by Oliver Summer Publishing.

ISBN: 978-1-5272-6043-6

www.forhelpwithanxiety.com

hello@forhelpwithanxiety.com

Authored by Ged Jenkins-Omar

Front Cover Photo by Aldain Austria on Unsplash

Back Cover Photo by Jakub Kriz on Unsplash

Disclaimer

The advice in this book should not replace proper medical advice from your doctor. It should not serve as medical advice or any form of medical treatment. Please always speak to your doctor before changing anything to do with your medical treatment. If you are taking medications, do not stop or change this without consulting your doctor. This book has been written and published strictly for informational and educational purposes only. Not all of the advice in this book will be suitable for you, so please use it as informational only and not as a substitute for individual therapy or medical care.

FOREWORD

By Ryan Ridgway

Having suffered with an anxiety disorder since the age of 12 years old I have had an extremely difficult journey in finding relief and support. I learned the hard way that there is no one cure, nor is that often realistic or possible.

Through many hours of research and lived experience I am now at peace with my anxiety and I have a collection of supportive ideas to use as and when I need them. All of these can be found here in this practical and enjoyable read.

'Help with Anxiety' has been written by a fellow sufferer and I have no doubt that within this book you will find some relief from your troublesome symptoms of anxiety.

You are stronger than your mind will have you believe and I am extremely confident that you could find your road to recovery within these pages.

Ryan Ridgway

Former Deputy Manager for the NHS 111 Service

Mental Health First Aid Trainer - Mental Health First Aid England

Please Read

Please be aware that some of the content in this book may resonate with you and momentarily trigger some of your symptoms of anxiety. If you start to feel distressed, emotional or become overwhelmed by the physical symptoms, thoughts, feelings or behaviours of anxiety, please be kind to yourself and take a break. This book is here to provide comfort and relief and there is no race to finish it. It is your companion. So, do read it, but read it at your own pace and in a space and moment that feels safe for you.

With love and thanks to Danielle, Oliver, and Summer – My absolute world & Universe.

Dedicated to Malcolm & Sharon.

TABLE OF CONTENTS

INTRODUCTION

Hello! Thank you for choosing to read this book, and I genuinely hope it helps you on your journey with your anxiety. I hope that it is informative and can help to change your life for the better, even if just a little bit. If only one tip out of the 150 in this book works for you and helps to improve your mental health, then that's amazing, but I hope you use and implement many more.

The coping strategies and tips listed in this book offer a mixture of techniques for immediate relief and more longer-term help in changing the way you think, act, and behave. Anxiety is vast, and sometimes you need a get out of jail free card for when a panic attack is on the horizon. Sometimes you need to make positive lifestyle changes. If you do not want to start taking an anti-anxiety medication or you do not like how the medication makes you feel. Or, if you would like some extra coping mechanisms as well as taking your regular medication, then this is the book for you.

It is essential to understand that anxiety is not a one size fits all mental health illness, and neither is coping with it. There will be tips and strategies in this book that work well for you and apply to your life, and there will be others that do not. However, what this book aims to do is educate you on the options that are available to you, so you can find the strategies that work for you. The tips written in this book are the result of self-experience, talks with friends and family, discussions with mental health professionals, and through thorough research.

I wanted to write this book as I have had my own journey and battles with anxiety. I have lived with it since my late teens and I suffered from it for many years. I am confident and outgoing but I still experience anxious thoughts, feelings and symptoms. The two sides do not exclude one another from occurring.

My anxiety grew from several factors. I watched a loved one die in front of me with their last words to me being 'Help me!'. This person was my Grandad and one of my superhero's. This along with experiencing near-death experiences, including being run over by a Range Rover while on a moped, led to me developing PTSD and health anxiety. Other factors played a role but a significant one is being diagnosed with a neurological condition called ataxia. My ataxia resulted from damage to the cerebellum in my brain which affects my nervous system. My symptoms of ataxia started when I was 22 years old but went undiagnosed, despite numerous tests, until I was 30. I lived for 8 years thinking I was going crazy, feeling fatigued, experiencing tremors and feeling like I was losing control of reality at times. This led to me developing severe anxiety and bouts of depression.

My anxieties piled up on top of me without me ever speaking about them or addressing them with myself or anyone else. I felt worse and worse up to the point where I just couldn't take it anymore. I've stared into the abyss, and for someone who has an absolute lust for life, I know what it takes to put someone there. I have previously used alcohol to cope and been unhealthily dependent on medications. Thankfully, I got through those dark days and although my anxiety is a part of me, I accept it, I manage it and I live my life freely, happily and successfully. I will have ataxia for the rest of my life and I still experience fatigue, dizziness and tremors. However, the type of ataxia I have is not progressive with a healthily lived life and thankfully not as severe as it could be.

I now have a great life with my wife and two children. I love my job at an animal sanctuary and I am an ambassador for a mental health charity. I can reflect on some amazing memories spending summers working abroad, getting a Guinness World Record and appearing in a film and on TV. But I can also reflect on how difficult my anxiety was at times and how life truly is a rollercoaster. Some days are amazing and some days are draining, but that is life.

Although I have a postgraduate degree in teaching my experience is not academic but based on a lived life and the miles walked in the shoes of someone who has experienced anxiety, panic attacks, fear, worry, fatigue, hyperventilation, dizziness, sweating, restlessness and every other imaginable symptom.

Our anxieties do not define us but they can make our journey difficult. Let this book help you to take back control and start living life to the fullest again and without fear.

If you need help immediately, then there is an index of available organisations at the back of this book for you. In the meantime, I wish you every success on your journey with your anxiety. I have every faith that you will learn to control it and cope with your thoughts, feelings and symptoms better than you are now. After all, remember, you are stronger than you know.

Positive mental health is wealth.

Best Wishes,

Ged

WHAT IS ANXIETY?

Anxiety is a nightmare. That's what anxiety is! It can make you feel full of panic, on edge, and like you are losing control of reality. It can give you strange aches and pains, make you feel breathless, dizzy and scared. It's a feeling of fear, worry and nervousness that something could potentially happen and you can't control its outcome. These fears and worries often stem from something that has happened to you, something you've seen, heard, or been involved in during your life.

It is a mental health illness that can be mild, moderate, or severe and can be a lone illness or coupled up with other physical or mental health illnesses. It can be debilitating, isolating, and make us feel like all hope is gone. It can also leave us feeling bitter and resentful and wondering why me? Studies have shown that an increase in anxiety could be linked to your stress levels or it might not? This is something to be mindful of though.

However, let us rewind for one second and just breathe in deeply...and then out. Anxiety, as horrible as it is, is the result of a function that has kept humans alive since the dawn of time. You may have heard of the fight or flight response, which is a physiological reaction that we all feel when we sense danger, a threat to our lives, or an imminent attack. This was great when we were running away from Saber-toothed Tigers in the Stone Age or for if our house or car is on fire right now. Rightly we would fight for our life or take flight and quickly. However, what has happened in the modern age with pressures, stresses, and technology flying in from all angles, is that our fight or flight response has gone into overdrive. This has caused us to become overwhelmed by our anxieties and worries and develop symptoms that are horrendous and compromise our mental health.

If you think of your fight or flight response as your inbuilt fire alarm. You want it to go off if there is a genuine fire, but you do not want it to go off every time you make your toast in the morning. We need it for genuine emergencies, but we don't need it ringing in our ears all of the time. If we look back at the famed and now extinct bird the Dodo, we can see why our inbuilt system is so important. The story has some variations to it but the tale suggests when human sailors first reached the beautiful island of Mauritius, they came across the Dodo, which was a flightless bird a bit bigger than a Turkey. The Dodo was not scared of humans or their dogs as they had no natural predators and thus perceived no threat. They had no inbuilt fight or flight system and were therefore very easy to catch and eat and, as a result, became extinct. This is a prime example of why we need our inbuilt alarm system, so we don't end up like the Dodo. However, we also don't want to feel full of fear, panic, be scared, and nervous all the time. Therefore, we need to find some peace and equilibrium in our lives.

Has your inbuilt alarm system gone into overdrive, leaving you feeling overwhelmed by your anxieties? If so, then hopefully, this book will go some way to providing you with the tips and tools that you need to bring calm to your life. So happy reading, happy learning, and let us find a place of balance for you between being a Dodo and being a continually ringing fire alarm.

Common types of anxiety

- General Anxiety Disorder (GAD)
- Social Anxiety
- Panic Disorder
- Post-Traumatic Stress Disorder (PTSD)
- Health Anxiety
- Obsessive Compulsive Disorder (OCD)
- Phobias including Agoraphobia
- Body Dysmorphic Disorder (BDD)

What are the symptoms of anxiety?

How we experience anxiety can differ from one person to the next. One thing is for sure. It can be terrifying; however we experience it. You might not experience all of these symptoms, and there may be others that you do feel, but here is a list of some of the most common:

Feeling:

Nervous, full of panic, on edge, scared, shaky, worried, like you're losing control, like you're going crazy, like you want to hurt yourself, like you might pass out, suicidal, hyperaware, fatigued, tired, weak, breathless, tight chested, nauseous, hollow, detached, cold or hot.

You might also suffer from:

Panic & anxiety attacks, an increased heart rate, palpitations, insomnia, rapid breathing or hyperventilation, diarrhoea, intrusive thoughts, a dry mouth, digestive problems, aches and pains, sweating, vomiting, slow memory recall, difficulty keeping still, difficulty relaxing, tingling sensations, headaches, light sensitivity, sound sensitivity, being overly aware of your heartbeat, repetitive thoughts, obsessions and compulsions.

YOUR COPING LIST

There are several ways in which you can read this book. You can pick it up at any page and learn a new strategy and tip. You can read it from cover to cover without making notes. Or you can read it and answer the questions that follow each tip. Whichever way you decide to read it, make sure to write down which strategies and tips help you to manage your anxiety and the things in your life that have a damaging effect on it. This will help you to complete your Coping List, which you can then use as your written anxiety help guide, referring to it whenever you need it.

Your Coping List

After reading through this book and finding the coping strategies and tips that work for you, write them here as an easy reference for if and when you need them. Please feel free to add more rows on paper or in your phone if you need to.

Coping Strategy	Page Number
Example – TALK TO SOMEONE	*Example – 16*
1	
2	
3	
4	
5	

6	
7	
8	
9	
10	
11	
12	
13	
14	
15	
16	
17	
18	
19	
20	

NOW WE HAVE COVERED
THAT, LET'S GET
STARTED…

THE MOST IMPORTANT?

The first six strategies and tips in this book are some of the most important to be aware of on your journey with anxiety.

#1
TALK TO SOMEONE

One of the most important coping mechanisms for people suffering with anxiety is talking to someone about it. You MUST speak to someone about how you are feeling. DO NOT bottle it all up inside as that will drive you crazy. Speak to a loved one or family member, a friend, a therapist, a doctor or someone else you trust. Talk to them all if you can. If you can't speak to someone close to you though, then there are various organisations you can reach out to and talk to like Mind, the Samaritans and more. There is an index of them available at the back of this book if you feel you need them. Whatever you do, make sure someone knows how you are feeling and do not keep it all inside. Remember a problem shared is a problem halved.

1. Have you spoken to someone about how you are feeling? YES/NO

2. Did it help you to feel less anxious or less worried about your feelings? YES/NO

3. Who did you speak to? What did they say?

4. Will you continue to speak them about how you are feeling? I am answering this one for you - YES.

5. Are you adding this strategy to your Coping List? Again, I am answering this one for you – YES.

#2
ACCEPT YOUR ANXIETY

One of the most effective coping strategies when dealing with anxiety is accepting it and not being fearful of it. Accept that you have anxiety. Accept that it is okay to feel the way you do. Accept that some days you will feel good and some days you will feel bad. Accept that there are strategies to help you cope with it. Accept that sometimes these strategies will work. Accept that sometimes they won't. Accept that anxiety is a part of you and you should love every part of you. But remember it does not define you and who you are. Practice positive affirmations like the ones described in this book and tell yourself daily that you accept your anxiety, you can cope with your anxiety and you are stronger for it. Tell yourself this every day until it becomes a reality.

---

1. Do you accept your anxiety? YES/NO

2. Do you accept that you will have good days and bad days? YES/NO

3. Do you accept that it is okay to feel the way you do? YES/NO

4. Are you adding your acceptance of your anxiety to your Coping List? YES/NO

#3
LEARN AND UNDERSTAND YOUR TRIGGERS

Understanding your triggers is extremely important in learning to live a happy life and coping with your anxiety. Does your anxiety stem from the way you look or the way you want to look? Does it come from thinking about something that has happened in your past? Or is it thinking about something that might happen in your future? Is it to do with a person or a group of people? Is it social media? Is it work? Is it social situations? Does a certain type of food or specific ingredient make you feel worse? Is it coffee, drugs or alcohol? Or is it something else? Whatever it is, the more you understand what triggers your anxious thoughts and feelings, the better armed you are to deal with it. Once you understand your triggers you can start to make positive changes to improve your situation. If you believe your triggers are related to something that you enjoy or have previously enjoyed doing, then look to manage them and do not necessarily completely avoid them. Complete avoidance can lead to you developing unhealthy opinions of certain places, people, things and more. Learn and understand your triggers as they may or may not be the root cause to your problems.

---

1. Will you take positive steps to manage your triggers? YES/NO

2. Are you adding this strategy to your Coping List? YES/NO

#4
FEELING SUICIDAL?

Although suicide has been a taboo subject in years gone by it shouldn't be in the modern age. In fact, having suicidal thoughts is probably more common than you think. A leading mental health charity reported following research that around 20 in every 100 people in the adult population will experience suicidal thoughts. It's important to understand though that having suicidal thoughts does not necessarily mean you want to act upon them. However, it is a signal that you might need help. If you are having suicidal thoughts then speak to someone who is supportive and if you don't have that someone in your life then there are plenty of helplines you can contact at the back of this book. If you are planning to act on it though or have already tried to act on it, seek help and support immediately. No matter how bad you feel right now, death is not the answer. There is help and support out there for you and people who love you and care for you. Even if you feel there isn't. Today may be the worst day ever, but it doesn't mean tomorrow will be. Remember, after a storm there is calm and the sun shines. Tomorrow could be that day.

---

1. Do you experience suicidal thoughts? YES/NO

2. Are you thinking about suicide at the moment? YES/NO

3. If YES to any of the above, please reach out to someone for support as soon as possible.

#5
EXERCISE

Exercise! Exercise! Exercise! Did I mention exercise? Producing endorphins in the body that act as a natural pain killer, stimulating anti-anxiety effects and improving our ability to sleep, exercise is your friend. Whether it's a walk, a run, weightlifting, a swim, yoga, kickboxing or any other form of exercise, it's time to treat your body to a good old workout. Make an effort, and your body and mind will reward you both physically and mentally, boosting your confidence and self-esteem as you go. If you prefer to work out alone, try walking, running, swimming or weightlifting. Or if you prefer to work out in a group, try something like boxing, yoga, fitness classes, football or a similar team sport. In looking for something to do there is lots of information available online to suit all abilities and workout videos that you can follow at home on YouTube. There will also be gyms, fitness classes and team sports in your local area that you can reach out to and get involved with.

---

1. Have you tried exercising? YES/NO

2. Did it help you to feel less anxious afterwards? YES/NO

3. Are you adding this strategy to your Coping List? YES/NO

#6
TRY AND GET ENOUGH SLEEP

Anxiety is tiring! Even after a great night's sleep, we can still feel exhausted from the daily battle that commences from the moment we wake up. With that said, it's essential to give our bodies the best possible chance to kick anxiety's butt, and that starts by getting 7-8 hours of unbroken sleep a night. This helps to keep us mentally well, maintaining our memory and boosting our immune system. However, sometimes this is not possible due to work, children, an overactive mind or something else. If you are struggling to get the sleep you need, then try using sleep aids. These include Chamomile, Lavender, Valerian, sleep music and breathing techniques. You should also avoid stimulants like drinking coffee and tea and reading or watching the news before going to bed. You should also limit screen time before bed as TV's, phones, laptops and tablets all produce blue light. This is reported to stimulate the mind and suppress the 'sleep hormone' melatonin which can lead to difficulty falling asleep and bouts of insomnia.

1. Do you regularly get 7-8 hours of unbroken sleep each night? YES/NO

2. If NO, will you be making positive changes to your sleeping habits? YES/NO

3. Are you adding this strategy to your Coping List? YES/NO

TAKE CONTROL

The strategies and tips in this section will teach you how to take control of your anxiety and manage it successfully.

#7
BALLOON METHOD

If you are experiencing negative thoughts but feeling creative, you can try letting go of them by using the Balloon Method. Firstly, write down what is making you feel anxious on a piece of paper. Then fold this paper up and put it in a helium balloon. Fill the balloon with helium using a canister from a supermarket and tie the end with string. Find a place outdoors where you feel comfortable and hold your balloon high in the sky. Then let go and say, "My thoughts do not control me. I control them, and I am letting them go". Then watch as your negative thoughts float away high into the sky and beyond your sight. If you do not have access to helium balloons then there is a smartphone app called Worry Float that offers the same process. These activities will not solve your anxiety in the long term; however, it might help you to feel empowered and start to take back control.

---

1. Have you tried this strategy? YES/NO

2. How did releasing the balloons make you feel?

3. Did it help you to feel empowered over your anxiety? YES/NO

4. Are you adding this strategy to your Coping List? YES/NO

#8
UNDERSTAND YOU ARE NOT ALONE

Something extremely important to remember when coping with your anxiety is that you are not alone. Although you may feel like you are going crazy and that the world is closing in on you try and remember that lots of other people feel like this to. Police officers, judges, doctors, lawyers, teachers, waste collectors, café assistants and more, all get the same feelings to. In the USA it is thought that around 1 in 5 people will suffer from anxiety in any given year and in the UK, it is around 1 in 6 in any given week. Something that is on the increase. By understanding you are not alone; you are opening yourself up to getting help and to talking about it with other people. Break down those barriers with your friends and family and speak openly about how you feel. You might be amazed at how many people you know feel the same way too.

---

1. Does understanding you are not alone help you to feel less anxious? YES/NO

2. Have you spoken to other people about how they feel and found commonalities with how you feel? YES/NO

3. If YES, how did this make you feel?

4. Will you speak to more people about how you feel? YES/NO

5. Are you adding this strategy to your Coping List? YES/NO

#9
UNDERSTAND IT'S OKAY NOT TO BE OKAY

As mentioned previously accepting your anxiety can really help you to cope with it. You are not crazy! You are not weird! You are not on your own! Sometimes there are things in our life that can affect how we feel, and sometimes we can't control them straight away. It's completely normal to have these feelings, and you must always know that it's okay not to be okay. Remember to tell yourself regularly that "It's okay not to be okay". There are so many quotes, memes, songs and videos that focus on this saying and with good reason. That's because IT'S okay not to be okay.

---

1. Do you understand that it's okay not to be okay? YES/NO

2. Does understanding this help you to feel more empowered and less anxious? YES/NO

3. Are you adding this strategy to your Coping List? YES/NO

#10
KEEP A DIARY

Keeping a physical diary will help you to keep track of how you are feeling. You can record anything in it that you notice triggers your anxiety and anything that helps to improve it. This will help you to manage your anxiety moving forward as you have a written record of what helps you and what doesn't, to reflect on. This book can be used as a diary where you can record what works for you and what triggers your anxiety. You can also use a real diary with the days and dates in and record your feelings this way. Another way you can keep a track of your triggers and coping mechanisms is by keeping a list on your phone that you can look at whenever you want and wherever you are. If you would like a more visual reminder on a day to day basis, you could try putting up a whiteboard or chipboard at home and writing them down in big letters on there.

---

1. Are you using this book or a diary to create your Coping List and track your triggers? YES/NO

2. Are you adding this strategy to your Coping List? YES/NO

#11
KEEP A MOOD CHART

Similarly, to tracking how you are feeling in a diary or through using this book, you can also try keeping a mood chart. This is a visual calendar where, at the end of each day, you can rate how anxious you have felt. You can do this by using the numbers 1 to 5 where one is 'Highly Anxious', and five is 'Not Anxious at All'. Concerning your rating, you can also write down what happened that day so you can see how your experiences, feelings and actions correlated to your anxiety levels. In looking for a mood chart to use there are free, downloadable and printable charts available online or you can get creative and make your own.

Try this strategy for at least two weeks before completing this section.

1. Did you note down how anxious you felt each day and how these correlated to your experiences, feelings and actions? YES/NO

2. Did recording your feelings like this help you to identify things that trigger your anxiety and things that help to improve it? YES/NO

3. Are you adding this strategy to your Coping List? YES/NO

#12
THE LAW OF ATTRACTION

There are lots of very successful people out there who live their lives by the Law of Attraction and swear that it works for them. But what is it? Well, in a nutshell, it is the idea that the actions, words and thoughts we emit into the universe will return to us multiplied. For example, if you regularly give money to charities, the universe will find a way to reward you back financially. On the flip side if you typically say nasty things about people, then the universe will return that nastiness to you multiplied. Whether or not this practice works is for you to decide; however, it can have merit when using it as a coping mechanism for anxiety. So, with this in mind, when thinking about your anxiety try and replace the negative thoughts, words and actions you put out into the universe with positive ones. Easier said than done, right? However, with practice, you can turn "I feel like I am dying" into "I have felt this before, I know it will pass, and I will feel amazing". The words and actions you emit will be personalised to you, so try and identify the things you say and do that are negative. Make a list of them and try and change them for more positive statements and actions. To further explore the Law of Attraction, you could try reading The Secret.

---

1. Are you adding this strategy to your Coping List? YES/NO

#13
TELL YOURSELF YOU ARE GREAT

Muhammad Ali truly believed he was the greatest, and he was the greatest. Why? Because he had great skill and great strength but also because he believed in himself and told himself and the world on a daily basis that he was the greatest. Now there are countless books on positive affirmations but in its purest form start to tell yourself that you are great. Every morning you wake up tell yourself that you are great, you feel great, you look great, you are healthy, you are stronger than anxiety, and you are going to have a great day. Do this every day, even if you don't believe it until it becomes a habit. This is a part of taking back control, and sooner or later, you will start to believe in your words. If you struggle to say these positive affirmations to begin with, then there are lots of videos on YouTube that you can follow along with. So even if you find it a bit strange at first you can listen to them online and repeat them out loud or in your head.

1. Have you been telling yourself you are great? YES/NO

2. Have you been repeating other positive affirmations to yourself? YES/NO

3. How do these make you feel?

4. Are you adding this strategy to your Coping List? YES/NO

#14
FEELINGS ARE NOT FACTS

Something fundamental to remember is that feelings are not scientific facts. Sometimes you can confuse what you think about yourself or what you think others think about you as facts. This is not the case. You may think you are dying when in fact you are very healthy. You may think that people hate you when in fact they like you and you are a lovely person. You might think that you are fat when you are a very healthy weight. Feelings are not necessarily facts. The next time you have anxious, negative and intrusive thoughts remember to tell yourself that feelings are not facts.

---

1. Are you going to tell yourself that feelings are not facts? YES/NO

2. Are you adding this strategy to your Coping List? YES/NO

#15
PRACTICE GRATITUDE

Sometimes it is hard when you are anxious and anxiety-ridden to be thankful for anything. However, in being thankful, you are opening yourself up to more positivity. Instead of thinking about the things that make you anxious and hating the fact that you are anxious, focus on the things that you are thankful for. For example, every morning, when you wake up say to yourself 'I am thankful for my friends, my dog, my family, my job, the sky and the birds that sing'. Or whatever you can find in your life to be thankful for. If you are struggling to find things in your life that you are thankful for now then try thinking about moments in the past that you have been thankful for. "I am thankful that I got to take that break I wanted and feel the sun on my back", "I am thankful that my mum and dad were great parents and raised me well", or whatever else you can think of. There is lots to be grateful for even in your darkest days, and you can use this to help you regain a more positive outlook on your life.

1. Do you have things in your life to be thankful for? YES/NO

2. What are they?

3. Are you going to take time out of your day to think about the things you are thankful for? YES/NO

4. Are you adding this strategy to your Coping List? YES/NO

#16
ALLOW THOUGHTS TO PASS IN AND OUT

Negative and anxious thoughts are going to occur. The trick is not to dwell on them and let them pass straight in and out instead. Accept that they will come into your mind but do not get stressed about them when they do. Understand that you are not alone in having them and that negative thoughts are as normal as having positive thoughts. As quickly as they flow in, let them flow out without paying them any more attention than they deserve. Once they have entered your mind, if they do not automatically leave then use a distraction technique like the ones in this book to change your thought process. Remember you are not alone in experiencing negative and anxious thoughts, so try not to overthink them or over-worry about them. Let them in, then let me out.

---

1. Do you understand that it is normal to have negative thoughts as well as positive ones? YES/NO

2. Have you tried letting your anxious and negative thoughts straight in and then straight out? YES/NO

3. Did you use distraction techniques to help you achieve this? YES/NO

4. If so, which ones?

5. Are you adding this strategy to your Coping List? YES/NO

#17
YOU ARE NOT HAVING A HEART ATTACK

If your anxiety results in you having a panic attack, recognise it as a panic attack and not anything more sinister. If you have experienced it before, then it will still be scary, but you may better equipped to deal with it. If it is the first time it has happened to you, you may think you are dying, having a heart attack or losing your mind. You may even phone an ambulance. In this instance, do whatever you need to do to get through it. If you need to call for help, phone for help. Reach out and get the care and support that you need. Moving forward, once you have experienced a panic attack previously and it occurs again, try and recognise it as a panic attack. Concentrate on your breathing and other techniques as covered in this book. If it is a panic attack, you are not dying, and you will recover within a short space of time even if it does not feel like it in the moment.

---

1. Have you had a panic attack before? YES/NO

2. Did you know it was a panic attack or did you think it was something else?

3. The next time you had a panic attack, did you recognise it as a panic attack? YES/NO

4. If you experience a panic attack again, will you recognise it as a panic attack and use the breathing strategies and other techniques in this book? YES/NO

5. Are you adding this strategy to your Coping List? YES/NO

#18
REPEAT A MANTRA

Learning a mantra that you can repeat in your head can help you when feeling anxious. A well-known one is "This too shall pass". Others are "I feel great", "I am healthy", "My life is wonderful". Even if you do not believe these at the moment say them anyway. Train your brain to say these mantras when negative thoughts try and penetrate your mind, and you will become stronger for it.

---

1. Have you decided which mantras you are going to say when you are feeling anxious? YES/NO

2. What are they?

3. Have you used them? YES/NO

4. How did they make you feel?

5. Will you repeat your mantras, when you are feeling anxious? YES/NO

6. Are you adding this strategy to your Coping List? YES/NO

#19
LEARN WHAT WORKS

There are lots of tips in this book – 150 to be precise. Hopefully, many of them will work for you, but many of them will not. The trick is to learn what works for you and to use this to your strengths. Having anxiety is not a one glove fits all illness, and neither is coping with it. There are various types of anxiety so you will need to find the strategies that work well for you. Try lots of techniques and methods until you find the glove that fits you best. Write them down on your Coping List at the beginning of this book and then use this list to help you manage your anxiety moving forward.

Once you have read all 150 strategies and tips in this book revisit these questions.

1. Have you tried lots of strategies and tips in this book? YES/NO

2. Have you implemented any in your life? YES/NO

3. Have you created your Coping List? YES/NO

4. If YES great, if NO what has stopped you?

5. Are you adding this strategy to your Coping List? YES/NO

#20
REMEMBER PANIC ATTACKS
ALWAYS END

Everything that has a start must have a finish, and your anxiety-induced panic or anxiety attack is just the same. As horrible as they are, they will pass. They may come again multiple times a day, once a month, more or less. But they will pass. If you have a panic or anxiety attack, use the tips in this book to help relieve the symptoms and get through it, and remember to try and tell yourself when it is happening – this will pass.

---

1. If you have had a panic or anxiety attack have you told yourself 'this will pass'? YES/NO

2. As horrible as it was did knowing it will pass help you to get through it? YES/NO

3. Are you adding this strategy to your Coping List? YES/NO

#21
ONLY DO AS MUCH AS YOU CAN DO

If you are feeling anxious remember to only do as much as you think you can do or want to do. It is okay not to be able to do everything and to allow yourself some space and time. Although it may be frustrating for you, you have to understand that in the short term there may be some limitations on the things that you can and can't do. What is important is to accept this and not let it get to you as this will only make you feel worse. Push yourself to do well, to achieve and to do things that you want to do. But do not push yourself too hard that it makes you feel anxious beyond your limits. Things will get better and improve for you but make life easier for yourself in the short term and do not put any additional pressure on yourself.

---

1. Do you recognise that sometimes you push yourself too much and make yourself feel more anxious as a result? YES/NO

2. In what situations do you do this?

3. Will you push yourself to achieve but not too much that you burn out with anxiety? YES/NO

4. Are you adding this strategy to your Coping List? YES/NO

#22
STAND UP STRAIGHT

When anxiety kicks in, we tend to hunch over, often crossing our arm or arms across our body and towards our shoulders as we fill with tension and nervousness. The reason we do this is a subliminal message to ourselves to protect our vital organs like our heart and our lungs as we enter our fight or flight mode. If you feel like this is the case, it is essential to offer our bodies a natural remedy to this. To do this try and stand up straight, taking a big deep breath in for four seconds. Then hold it in for four seconds as you stand solidly, puff out your chest, pull your shoulders back and then exhale for four seconds. This signals to our mind that we are in fact in control of our body. You can then try and follow this up with other techniques as described in this book.

Try this strategy at least three separate times before completing this section.

1. Did this strategy help you to feel more in control of your body? YES/NO

2. Did it help you to feel less anxious? YES/NO

3. Are you adding this strategy to your Coping List? YES/NO

#23
BE AROUND PEOPLE THAT MAKE YOU FEEL SAFE

Having anxiety or any mental health or physical health problem often requires support from those around us. If you are lucky enough to have a support network around you, share your feelings with them and spend time with them. The people who love you and understand you will help you to feel better about your situation and often help you find the proper support you need. Some may have even bought you this book. The people we surround ourselves with are a significant influence on how we feel and how we behave. So, with that in mind, surround yourself with support and love and empathy where you can. If you feel alone or do not have a support network around you, please see the list of organisations at the back of this book. They will be able to help you and offer you the support you need.

1. Are you spending enough time with people who love and care for you? YES/NO

2. Have you shared with them how you truly feel? YES/NO

3. If NO, are you going to tell them how you feel? YES/NO

4. If you have told them how you feel, did you feel supported? YES/NO

5. Are you adding this strategy to your Coping List? YES/NO

#24
STOP COMPARING YOURSELF TO OTHEK

This may or may not be the root cause of your anxiety, but comparing yourself to others definitely won't help your situation either. We can often be guilty of concerning ourselves with the perceived success of others and then questioning our own lives as a result. This can lead to feelings of anxiety and inferiority as we wish that we lived other people's lives. As the old saying goes, comparison is the thief of joy, and if you have anxiety, you need to focus on working on yourself and bringing joy into your life. Not looking at what others do or have. Do not waste your time envying other people's lives as there are most likely things in your life that they wish for and that you would never ever know. Remember that around 1 in 5 people (and maybe higher) will be suffering from anxiety problems. So, you might actually find that those you are comparing yourself to may just be as anxious as you, or even worse.

---

1. Do you find yourself comparing your life to other people's lives? YES/NO

2. How does this make you feel?

3. Are you going to try and stop comparing your life to other people's lives? YES/NO

4. Are you adding this strategy to your Coping List? YES/NO

#25
WRITE IT OUT

Lots of people who suffer from anxiety find that writing helps them to cope with feelings that are otherwise trapped inside. In writing creatively, they find that they can express how they are feeling, which helps to self soothe as well as exploring their anxiety through words. Try taking a pen and paper or writing on your phone and just see where your words take you. Even if you have never done something like this before, maybe it is time to start? You do not have to share your words with anyone else unless you want to. However, writing freely and expressively may help to have a positive impact on your overall mental health and anxiety.

---

1. Have you ever written about your feelings before? YES/NO

2. Are you going to try and write about how you feel? YES/NO

3. If you have tried this strategy did it help you to express your feelings? YES/NO

4. Will you continue to write about how you feel? YES/NO

5. Are you adding this strategy to your Coping List? YES/NO

#26
SEE THE BIGGER PICTURE

Just as you may look at other people and see good things in them, people will look at you and see good things in you. Whether you believe this or not, it will be true. Sometimes we allow our anxiety to become overwhelming, and it can make us feel inadequate, when in fact, the opposite is true. Try and see the bigger picture, as even in your worst moments, there will be people who admire you and wished they had the strength that you have.

---

1. Does your anxiety sometimes make you feel inadequate? YES/NO

2. Do you recognise that you are amazing and have lots to offer? YES/NO

3. If NO, ask your friends and family what they think is great about you.

4. What did they say?

5. How did this make you feel?

6. Are you adding this strategy to your Coping List? YES/NO

#27
KEEP A TIDY HOME, WORK SPACE AND CAR

A chaotic home, work space or car can all contribute to a chaotic mind. If your house, work space or car is full of rubbish or just generally untidy, then it is time to get cleaning to improve your surroundings to enhance your mental health. We spend most of our lives in our homes, at work and in our cars and if we are surrounded by rubbish, it can add to our anxiety and leave us feeling overwhelmed and unmotivated. These are all places that we need to feel relaxed in and let's be honest tidying up is not that difficult once we get that initial get up and go. Not only can cleaning be therapeutic, calming our minds, but the result provides us with a better environment to be in. So, make these environments a place you can feel relaxed in and not one that adds to your already anxious life.

---

1. Is your home, work space or car untidy? YES/NO

2. Are you going to make an extra effort to clean these areas? YES/NO

3. How did you feel once you cleaned these areas?

4. Are you adding this strategy to your Coping List? YES/NO

#28
PHONE SOMEONE YOU TRUST

If you are feeling anxious or worried, then it's always good to have someone on hand who you can phone and talk to. Having someone who understands your situation and who you can talk to about how you are feeling can stop you from feeling both anxious and isolated. If there are opportunities to speak to people face to face then do so. But for times when you are on your own then have a designated person or people that you can ring when you are feeling full of anxiety. Once you have decided on who your 'phone a friend' will be, it would be useful for you to give them this book so they can familiarise themselves with strategies and techniques to help you when you are having a bad day. If you feel that you have not got anyone to speak to about your anxiety then there are groups and phone numbers in this book that you can contact to seek help. Remember a problem shared is a problem halved and you will often feel better, even if only a little if you share how you feel with someone else.

---

1. Do you have someone you can phone if you are having a bad day? YES/NO

2. Who can you phone?

3. Have you offered them the opportunity to read this book so that they can learn strategies and techniques to help support you? YES/NO

4. Are you adding this strategy to your Coping List? YES/NO

#29
DO NOT BE SCARED OF ANXIETY

Easier said than done, right? Especially as you feel yourself being swallowed up by the world, sent into panic and into what feels like a near-death experience. However, do not be scared by your anxiety as it will not kill you, and you will learn to manage it successfully. Anxiety should be scared of you! Scared of how strong you are and how each day, your coping mechanisms improve as you learn more techniques and become better equipped to look after your mental health. Tell it right now, 'I am not scared of my anxiety!'. Take ownership of it. It may be a part of you, but it isn't the whole of you. Accept it and face it head-on and do not let it overcome you. You've got this!

1. Are you scared of your anxiety? YES/NO

2. What is it that scares you?

3. Are you going to remove the fear from your anxiety by learning lots of coping strategies like the ones in this book? YES/NO

4. Say to yourself now, "I am not scared of my anxiety".

5. Are you adding this strategy to your Coping List? YES/NO

#30
JOIN ONLINE ANXIETY GROUPS

In these modern times, we are fortunate to have a world of information and networks at our fingertips. You can use this to your advantage by finding groups and forums online where people are suffering from anxiety just like you are. Facebook is a good place for this as there are lots of pages you can follow for information and encouragement. There are also groups that you can join where you can talk about your anxiety with likeminded people. If you are already on Facebook, then type 'Anxiety' into the search bar and join the groups that look suitable for you. If you haven't got a Facebook account, then it might be worthwhile creating one and completing the search as above. There will also be other forums and groups available on other websites, so do your research and find out which ones suit you best. Please be careful of Googling symptoms though and only take specific medical advice from professionals and not fellow sufferers.

---

1. Have you joined any online anxiety groups or forums? YES/NO

2. Which ones have you joined?

3. Are you adding this strategy to your Coping List? YES/NO

#31
KNOWLEDGE IS POWER

In learning about your anxiety and panic attacks, you will come to understand why you are feeling the way you are, and this is important. It is essential to realise that you are not dying, you are not weird and that there may be additional triggers causing you to feel the way you do. Having a better understanding of your mental health will help you to stay calm and prevent your anxiety from freaking you out as much as it has been doing. Read books like this one, professional articles, blogs, and talk and listen to medical professionals and other likeminded people. By learning, understanding and applying the strategies in this book and other similar self-help books and by speaking to professionals and other people about their coping mechanisms you will be in a better position to cope with your anxiety. Knowledge is power.

---

1. Do you have a good understanding of your anxiety? YES/NO

2. Do you know why you feel the way you do? YES/NO

3. If YES does this help you to manage it more successfully? YES/NO

4. If NO Are you going to do more research into why you feel the way you do? YES/NO

5. Are you adding this strategy to your Coping List? YES/NO

#32
BE PATIENT

Learning to cope with your anxiety and understanding it is a gradual process, and it will not happen overnight. You are going to have good, bad, great and terrible days so be patient. Learn your techniques, understand your anxiety and enjoy the mini wins as they come along. As mentioned previously it's okay not to be okay, and there are lots of other people out there who are experiencing the same horrible feelings that you are. You will improve over time and get better at kicking anxiety's butt; however, be patient in the meantime and appreciate you are not going crazy.

---

1. How long have you been suffering from your anxiety?

2. Do you understand that you need to be patient and that you will improve with time? YES/NO

3. Are you actively learning strategies and techniques to help you manage your anxiety? YES/NO

4. Are you adding this strategy to your Coping List? YES/NO

#33
JOIN A SUPPORT GROUP

There are lots of support groups out there for all types of needs whether that be for people with anxiety, depression, stress or something else. There is a list of support organisations at the back of this book that will be able to signpost you to groups near where you live. Or you can also use the internet to find groups where you can speak to likeminded people. By participating in groups like these, it will help you to open up about how you are feeling while reducing feelings of isolation and being judged. This can have a positive effect on your anxiety as you discover that other people feel the same way you do. You can share coping mechanisms, strategies and stories and help to support each other.

---

1. Would you like to join a support group? YES/NO

2. Have you found a suitable group in your local area? YES/NO

3. Are you going to attend the group? YES/NO

4. If you attended a group, how did this make you feel?

5. Will you attend more support groups? YES/NO

6. Are you adding this strategy to your Coping List? YES/NO

#34
LOOK FOR A LESS STRESSFUL JOB

Does your job stress you out beyond your comfort levels? Do you find yourself wishing you did something else? Do you feel undervalued? All of these things can add to your stress levels which can have a negative effect on your anxiety. If this is you, maybe it's time to look for a new job or role that has a more positive impact on your mental health. Luckily in this day and age, opportunities are everywhere. Whether that is working for someone else or working for yourself doing something you have always wanted to do. You might not become a billionaire (or you might?), but you may find happiness in something like starting your own upcycling business or working in a caring environment. Money is not everything. As long as you can cover the basics, the most important things in your life should be your health, happiness, wellbeing, your family and friends. Everything material is just a bonus. Remember, positive mental health is wealth.

---

1. Does your job make you feel anxious? YES/NO

2. Would you preferably do another job? YES/NO

3. If YES, what would you love to do?

4. Are you adding this strategy to your Coping List? YES/NO

#35
THROW IT IN THE BIN

Get a piece of paper. Get a pen. Write down everything that you feel anxious about. Screw up the paper. Throw it in the bin. Breathe. If only that could cure your anxiety and things were that simple. Now although this will not cure your anxiety, studies have suggested that this act of physically discarding your negative thoughts away can have an empowering effect on you. Of course, thoughts can regenerate and very quickly, but it might be worth trying and seeing how you feel? This might just be the first act that kickstarts you to taking back control of your life.

---

1. Have you tried writing your anxieties down and throwing them in the bin? YES/NO

2. Did this help you to feel empowered? YES/NO

3. Are you adding this strategy to your Coping List? YES/NO

#36
FORGIVE OR FORGET

Most of us will have come across people or situations that we believe have wronged us in our life. Some of us find it easier to forgive and forget than others, and some of us hold deep grudges, sometimes for a lifetime. If you are holding deep grudges about someone or a situation that has wronged you, then you need to try and let these go or resolve them. Harbouring ill feelings towards others or a negative situation is not prosperous for moving forward with your life. These feelings may even be about something you have done or not done. These can all add additional stress and pressure to your anxieties and insecurities, which you are working hard to combat. If you can identify with this situation, then it is time to address it face on and either forgive or forget. Or you can continue to allow them to make you feel anxious and miserable, sometimes for a lifetime.

---

1. Do you have negative feelings towards a person that is or has been in your life? YES/NO

2. Do you have negative feelings towards yourself or a situation that has happened in your life? YES/NO

3. Is it time to forgive or forget and move forward? YES/NO

4. Are you adding this strategy to your Coping List? YES/NO

#37
INTRUSIVE THOUGHTS

The more you try and tell yourself not to think about something, the more you will think about it. Can you relate to that? That's because the more we tell ourselves not to think about something, the more we are actually thinking about it and focussing on it. It is entirely normal to have intrusive thoughts, and they are not a reflection of how you truly feel. Often your intrusive thoughts may be the complete opposite of how you want to think or feel. However, our brains like to play challenging games with us. The best thing that you can do is to allow your intrusive thoughts to pass in and then pass out again. These thoughts may be troubling, make you feel emotional or make you feel a terrible person. However, the more we pay them attention, the more they will keep coming back and hurting us. To break this chain, we can use various strategies including talking therapy, distraction techniques, breathing techniques and other strategies as outlined in this book. If your intrusive thoughts are becoming unbearable though, the more critical it is to talk about them with someone you trust.

1. Do you suffer from intrusive thoughts? YES/NO

2. Have you been able to become at ease with them? YES/NO

3. If NO you need to speak to someone about them.

4. Are you adding this strategy to your Coping List? YES/NO

#38
COLD WATER THERAPY

It might sound a bit chilly at first but studies have suggested that taking cold showers and immersing ourselves in cold water can actually boost our mental wellbeing. This is because as we come into contact with the cold water it is suggested to release endorphins and help decrease our levels of cortisol, a hormone responsible for stress and pain. There are lots of studies around this subject and it is also worth looking into a man called Wim Hof. The Iceman as he is also known is probably the leading figure behind promoting the benefits of cold water therapy. If you would like to try this strategy you could start by taking a cold shower every morning and looking into Wim Hof and his teachings for more information.

---

1. Have you tried cold water therapy? YES/NO

2. How did this make you feel?

3. Will you continue to do this? YES/NO

4. Are you adding this strategy to your Coping List? YES/NO

#39
PAY YOUR BILLS

Having anxiety is challenging enough already; therefore, anything you can do in your life to avoid adding to it should be prioritised. With that in mind if you have outstanding bills or you are in debt, then you need to face this head-on and get them sorted. Pay your bills as they come in and make sure your finances do not cause you even more anxiety. If you are already in a financial pickle, then speak to the Citizens Advice Bureau or another similar organisation who can help you with your finances. There is lots of help out there. Do what you need to do. Depending on what you think about it, money won't necessarily buy you happiness, but by not being in control of it, it can make you more anxious.

1. Do you pay your bills as they come in? YES/NO

2. Are you in unmanageable debt? YES/NO

3. How does this make you feel?

4. Are you going to reach out for help and face it head-on? YES/NO

5. Are you adding this strategy to your Coping List? YES/NO

#40
STOP CATASTROPHISING

Something 99.9% of people with anxiety are guilty of doing is catastrophising. This is where our thoughts always end up in the worst-case scenario. Catastrophising can occur over things that are happening in the present or over something that you think might happen in the future. Examples of catastrophising over things that are happening in the present might include thinking that you are about to die, when in fact, you are having a panic attack. On the other hand, you may catastrophise over imaginary events that could occur in the future. Examples of this could be, what if my partner cheats on me and leaves me all alone? What will I do? Or what if I lose my job and all of my income? How will I support my family? To stop catastrophising, firstly you need to recognise when you are doing it. If you find your thoughts spiralling to the worst-case scenario, you need to say to yourself "I am catastrophising". In realising, you are catastrophising; you can then bring yourself back down to a more level headed way of thinking by using a variety of methods as outlined in this book. These include being mindful, meditation, breathing and distraction techniques and other strategies.

---

1. Do you often catastrophise? YES/NO

2. Are you adding this strategy to your Coping List? YES/NO

#41
BE OPEN AND HONEST WITH THOSE AROUND YOU

By accepting your anxiety and opening up to those around you and telling them that you have anxiety, you are opening yourself up to more support and more help. For some people opening up about their mental health is easy but for many others it is not. There are several reasons you might find opening up difficult. You might not want to burden those close to you with how you feel, or you might worry that people will see you as weak or weird. There may be other reasons. However, one thing you should understand is that you are not burdening anyone you speak to, you are empowering them to help you. You are also not weak or weird but extremely strong and very normal, with around 1 in 5 people (or more) suffering from the same condition in any given year. Anxiety can make us feel closed in, but the more open you are about it, the less closed in your world will feel.

---

1. Have you opened up to those around you about how you feel? YES/NO

2. If YES great, if NO, are you going to? YES/NO

3. If YES, did this help you to feel more in control of your anxiety? YES/NO

4. Are you adding this strategy to your Coping List? YES/NO

#42
PUT YOUR POSITIVE MOMENTS IN A JAR

If you are feeling anxious every day and you are struggling to see the light at the end of your tunnel, try writing down one positive moment out of your day and putting it in a jar. If you can't find a positive in a day, then try in a few days or even a week and slowly build your jar up. As time goes by, when you are feeling particularly anxious, or if you are having an awful day then get your jar out and read and remember all the beautiful things in your life that you can be thankful for. This might not help you if you are in a state of panic; however, it might help you to raise your mood if your anxiety is making you feel depressed.

1. Have you started writing down your positive moments and putting them in a jar? YES/NO

2. Once your jar is starting to fill up, have you looked back on your positive moments? YES/NO

3. How did reading them make you feel?

4. Did it help to raise your mood? YES/NO

5. Are you adding this strategy to your Coping List? YES/NO

#43
TAKE A MENTAL HEALTH DAY

If we have the flu and our body is aching, we tend to take a day off work. If we have Norovirus or some other form of stomach illness or diarrhoea, we take time off work. However, if we are feeling anxious and stressed, we tend to push ourselves to our limits and go into work, often making ourselves feel worse in the process. Getting on with things is great, and for some people can be a coping strategy in itself. However, sometimes it's okay to take a mental health sick day. When all is said and done, you cannot be the best you in life or work if you are close to burning out. You do not have to tell your boss the real reason if you do not want to, but hopefully, you can, and they will be understanding. It is also worth speaking to your workplace and asking if there is a qualified mental health first aider you can talk to. If there isn't you could ask if this is something they could explore as a lot more businesses are putting this in place. This strategy might be harder for those of you who are self-employed but, in this instance, see if a family member or friend can help you out. If this is not possible, try and work a half-day as opposed to a full day. The money will come and go, but your health is something you need to prioritise. Remember to be kind to yourself.

1. The next time you feel like you are burning out, are you going to take a mental health day? YES/NO

2. Are you adding this strategy to your Coping List? YES/NO

#44
READ SELF-HELP BOOKS

Just as you are doing right now. In reading this book, you are learning more about anxiety and how to cope with it. As the wise old saying goes, knowledge is power, and by reading books on anxiety, you are gaining more control over your anxiety. There are several books out there that can teach you a variety of techniques and are written by experienced professionals covering their various specialisms in depth. If you are looking for more self-help books then just go on Amazon or any book site, type in 'anxiety books' and find the ones that look like they will suit you the best.

---

1. Have you read any other self-help books on anxiety? YES/NO

2. What books have you read?

3. Did they help you to cope with your anxiety? YES/NO

4. Are you adding this strategy to your Coping List? YES/NO

#45
PERFECTION IS NOT POSSIBLE

It doesn't matter what we look like, how talented we are, or how much money there is in our bank accounts. Perfection in everything is impossible. With that in mind, it's time to give yourself a break from trying to be a perfect kind of you. We all have imperfections, but some of us let them affect us more than others. It's time to be kinder to yourself and allow yourself good days as well as bad days. Anxiety is hard enough without beating yourself up daily.

1. Do you often worry that you do not have a perfect life? YES/NO

2. Do you often worry that you do not look perfect? YES/NO

3. Do you need to give yourself a break and stop beating yourself up? YES/NO

4. Do you need to be kinder to yourself? YES/NO

5. Are you adding this strategy to your Coping List? YES/NO

#46
SET SMALL DAILY GOALS

If your anxiety is overwhelming and the days of misery are turning into weeks and months of suffering, it's time to look for those mini wins in your day. We can easily get caught up in a vicious cycle of feeling anxious and feeling negative about our anxiety, so we need to find positive moments in our day to help break this chain of despair. One way you can do this is by setting yourself small daily goals. Whether that's getting out of bed, making a freshly cooked meal, going to the gym, trying some yoga at home, sorting out your bills, reading a book about anxiety or something else. Depending on how you are feeling and how much energy you have, try and give yourself at least one goal for the day and add more as you feel more energetic. Write them down in your phone or on a piece of paper in the morning and as you complete each task, be sure to feel a sense of achievement. Know that even on a day when you can feel anxious you can still achieve whatever you put your mind and body to.

---

1. Have you started to set yourself small daily goals? YES/NO

2. What types of goals do you set?

3. How do you feel when you have completed them?

4. Are you adding this strategy to your Coping List? YES/NO

#47
DEVELOP YOUR OWN TECHNIQUES

There may be lots of techniques and strategies in this book to help you cope with your anxiety, but there will also be tips and tricks that you have developed yourself and that work well for you. If this is the case, then have faith in your strength and ability to manage your anxiety using these strategies. Just because you haven't seen them written in a book or heard about them elsewhere, it doesn't mean they aren't just as good as some of the more well-known techniques. You do what works for you. You are the captain of your ship, and you know what works for you and what doesn't. Listen to your body and mind and put faith in yourself and your strategies.

---

1. Do you have some coping techniques that work well for you? YES/NO

2. What are they?

3. Do they help you to manage your anxiety? YES/NO

4. Are you going to keep using them? YES/NO

5. Are you adding this strategy to your Coping List? YES/NO

#48
MAKE A PLAN

Ever heard of the 7 P's? Proper Planning and Preparation Prevents P*ss Poor Performance? Well, now you have. This is a saying used by the military, business people, marketers, coaches, personal trainers and many other professionals and people who aspire to be better versions of themselves. It is also something that anyone with anxiety should think about implementing in their own lives. In reading this book, you will be learning lots of coping techniques and strategies that can help you when you are having anxious thoughts or a panic attack. Many of them you can plan into your day to help you manage your anxiety, and many of them you can use for when your anxiety becomes overwhelming, and you need to bring yourself back down again. Your Coping List at the start of this book will help you to formulate your plan, but it is down to you to action it. A daily plan might look something like; eating anxiety fighting foods, avoiding your triggers, exercising, taking time out to be mindful, and so on. It might also include a plan for if you feel your anxiety becoming overwhelming or if you are having a panic attack including; breathing techniques, speaking to someone, switching off your social media or something else. Whatever you do, plan ahead and take control of your anxiety.

---

1. Are you adding this strategy to your Coping List? YES/NO

#49
CREATE A TIMELINE

Whatever has happened in your life, something has led to you developing anxious feelings. Maybe you know what it is; perhaps you don't? Maybe it's something monumental, perhaps it's something small. Or perhaps it is lots of little things that have all mixed into a recipe of anxiety. Whatever it is, it might be helpful for you to create a timeline and list all the things that have happened to you over the years as you try to identify where your anxiety may have stemmed from. This might help you to put your anxiety into context and understand why you feel the way you do. It will also help you to address your anxiety and open yourself up to reaching out for specific help if you need it. Using a pen and paper write down all of the things that have happened to you in your life in age order, the good and the bad. Then see if you can identify where and why your anxious feelings may have started. Add as many things as possible no matter how big or small you think they may be and reflect on them.

---

1. Have you been able to identify moments that may have led to your anxious thoughts and feelings? YES/NO

2. Are you adding this strategy to your Coping List? YES/NO

#50
SURROUND YOURSELF WITH SUPPORT

The much-celebrated motivational speaker Jim Rohn famously quoted 'You are the average of the five people you spend the most time with'. Whether true or not, this quote is something worth keeping in mind for those of us with anxiety, as who we surround ourselves with can reflect on how we feel and think. If you surround yourself with negative and unsupportive people, this can lead to you feeling negative and unsupported. On the flip side, if you surround yourself with positive and supportive people, this can help you to feel more positive about your situation and supported with your needs. If there are people or relationships in your life that you think are negative, poisonous and affecting your anxiety then you need to address these. If you do not believe these people will change their ways, then you need to remove all negativity from your life and move forward with positive and supportive friends and family only.

---

1. Do you have any negative or unsupportive people in your life? YES/NO

2. Should you think about talking to them or removing them from your life? YES/NO

3. Do you have any positive and supportive people in your life? YES/NO

4. Can you spend more time speaking to them? YES/NO

5. Are you adding this strategy to your Coping List? YES/NO

#51
WORRY TIME AND WORRY-FREE TIME

There are two sides to this strategy. On one side is worry time, and the other is worry-free time. But what are they? Well, worry time is where you allocate a specific time in the day to worry or think about your anxieties. To use this strategy, throughout the day make a note of your worries on paper or in your phone and then come back to them at a specific time, later on. Do not think about them at the time they occur, but take control over them and know that you will revisit them later. When you do revisit them, think about them mindfully and use a breathing technique as shown in this book and make sure that you are relaxed. There are smartphone apps that can help you with this and one in particular worth getting is WorryTime by reachout.com. On the flip side, worry-free time is a time for you to do something that you enjoy and can distract you from your worries. It should be something that takes a bit of concentration, but that makes you feel good or rewarded for doing it. Worry-free activities might include playing an instrument, swimming, doing puzzles, reading, painting, getting creative or something else. Make sure to build half an hour or an hour of worry-free time into your day to give you a break from your anxious thoughts.

---

1. Are you adding either or both of these strategies to your Coping List? YES/NO

#52
EXPOSURE THERAPY

If your anxieties make you avoid places, people, situations or things, then exposure therapy can help you to address this. While avoiding these things can help us to feel safer in the short term, over a more extended period of time we may come to think of them as more dangerous than they are and this can lead to us having lower levels of confidence. If you are avoiding things that you would like to do then exposure therapy might be for you. An example of this might be that you are scared of going to a large shopping centre as you think you might pass out, die or lose your mind when in there. This might force you to avoid it entirely and have negative feelings towards it. If this is the case, you could start with more manageable objectives, then move on to more challenging goals. To start with you might go to the shopping centre with a friend but just stay in the car park for a little while. Then the next time you might walk up and touch the door. Then the time after that you might decide to go at the quietest time and then go inside the door for a few minutes. Then the next time you might go inside the door for 10 minutes and so on. You want to build this up until you can stay within the environment or situation without feeling full of panic and fear.

---

1. Are you adding this strategy to your Coping List? YES/NO

#53
CREATE LONG TERM GOALS

While our anxieties often focus on worrying about what might happen and what could happen in the future, we should also look positively towards the future by creating long term goals. Even at your lowest point, there will be things that you want to achieve in your life or something that you wish could happen. Make these your goals. Maybe you would like to get back driving after being too scared? Buy that dream home? Find Mr or Mrs Right after being heartbroken? Set up a successful business despite being afraid of failure? Travel abroad and go on a plane despite your fears? Or something else? Your goals don't necessarily have to be tied to your anxieties, but they can be. Whatever your dreams are, set them as targets that you can work towards and believe in them. It doesn't matter if it takes months, years or longer to reach your goals as long as you are focussed on them. By having something to aim towards you are giving your anxious life something positive to focus on, and this should not be underestimated. You are stronger than you know, so set those goals, no matter how big or small they are and work your way towards them.

1. Have you created some long-term goals? YES/NO

2. What are they?

3. Are you adding this strategy to your Coping List? YES/NO

#54
HAVE A ROUTINE

Having a routine can be helpful for those of us who suffer from anxiety as it can give us structure to our day. When looking at creating your routine, you should include all of the things that can have a positive impact on how you feel. This might be a shower or some breathing exercises every morning. Followed by planning a couple of relaxation breaks into your day while at work, at home or somewhere else. These might be at 10 am, and 3 pm and are moments where you have 10 minutes relaxation and close your eyes and breathe mindfully. At some point in the day, you might do some exercise. This might be every morning, lunchtime or evening. You could also plan some worry-free time into your day, which is half an hour or an hour where you do something that you enjoy. This could be drawing, playing an instrument, listening to music, reading a book, baking or something else. You could also decide to turn your phone and all social media platforms off at a certain time. You might even set a certain amount of time aside to work through your bills or housework so that they do not pile on top of you as time passes by. However your routine looks will be personal to you but make sure that it has a positive impact on your anxiety. Try and follow it as best you can but do not be too strict with it as you do not want to feel down if you miss part of it out.

1. Are you adding this strategy to your Coping List? YES/NO

DISTRACTION

The strategies and tips in this section will teach you distraction techniques that you can use when you find your anxious thoughts becoming overwhelming and intrusive. You can also use them if you feel an anxiety or panic attack coming on. These are in the moment strategies, and although effective, they should be used alongside other methods in this book for managing your anxiety long term.

#55
MEMORISE A LIST

If you can feel a panic attack creeping up or negative thoughts pecking at your head like an annoying repetitive Woodpecker then distraction techniques can work well. To start with you could try and replace your negative thoughts by memorising a list of words or things that mean something to you and saying them in your head. Perhaps you have a favourite sports team? Try learning all of the player's names and work your way through the team saying their names in your head. Maybe it's a recipe? Try working your way through the ingredients and how you would make the dish. Whatever it is, make it something that you genuinely like and is relatable to your life. You can also use this technique with numbers, your family member's names, your friend's birthdays, or something else you can come up with. By concentrating your attention on to something else other than your anxiety, you are breaking your anxious thoughts and allowing yourself to calm down. If you find it easier, you can also write these lists down on paper, which also gives your hands something to do.

Try this strategy at least three separate times before completing this section.

1. Did this strategy help to distract your mind from your anxious thoughts? YES/NO

2. Are you adding this strategy to your Coping List? YES/NO

#56
PICTURE A HAPPY MOMENT

This is probably one that you think a therapist might lie you down on a couch and ask you to do. So, do it. If you are feeling anxious or stressed, try closing your eyes and picturing a happy moment in your life. Think about a time when you enjoyed yourself and make sure to smile while you are thinking about it. Try replacing your negative thoughts with happy and positive thoughts. If you struggle to picture a happy moment in your head, try looking at photographs that remind you of a happy time in your life. Remember that good things happen for you to. Try coupling this strategy with a breathing technique to feel even more relaxed.

Try this strategy at least three separate times before completing this section.

1. Did this strategy help to distract your mind from your anxious thoughts? YES/NO

2. Did you think of a happy place, memory or use photographs?

3. What did you think about or what photographs did you look at?

4. Are you adding this strategy to your Coping List? YES/NO

#57
LOOK AROUND YOU

If you cannot escape your anxious thoughts or you feel like a panic attack is coming on, then try and focus on the things that are around you. Try and replace your growing thoughts of worry and nervousness with facts about what you can see. For example, I can see a picture on the wall. The image is square and has a sun on it. Underneath the sun is the sea. The sea is blue, and the waves are washing up on a sandy shore. This distraction technique can help you to replace your negative feelings with facts about what is around you. Try coupling this strategy with a breathing technique to feel even more relaxed. If you struggle to find something to focus on, then try another distraction technique like the ones written in this book.

Try this strategy at least three separate times before completing this section.

1. Did this strategy help to distract your mind from your anxious thoughts? YES/NO

2. Did this strategy help you to feel less anxious? YES/NO

3. Did it help you to avoid having a panic attack? YES/NO

4. Are you adding this strategy to your Coping List? YES/NO

#58
THE MAGIC WAND

When negative thoughts come into your head, imagine you have a magic wand that you can pull them out with. Then with a flick of the wand and saying 'Be gone!' throw them away into the air. By carrying out this action, you are taking control of your thoughts and discarding the negative ones away. If you do not want to physically do this due to other people being around, or you feel silly, then try and imagine that you are doing it instead.

Try this strategy at least three separate times before completing this section.

1. Did this strategy help to distract your mind from your anxious thoughts? YES/NO

2. Did this strategy help you to feel less anxious? YES/NO

3. Did it help you to avoid having a panic attack? YES/NO

4. Are you adding this strategy to your Coping List? YES/NO

#59
STAMP ON THE SPOT

It sounds crazy but let's face it; you probably feel like you are going crazy anyway. However, studies have suggested that stamping on the spot for a minute can help you to release stress hormones and anxiety that is pent up within your body. You might want to do this on your own, within your home or even in a toilet at work but give it a go. You can even do this with a friend or by helping someone else experiencing anxiety or a panic attack. When stamping, you can also try coupling this technique up with another distraction technique to divert your thoughts and completely override your anxious feelings. So, what are you waiting for? Get stamping.

Try this strategy at least three separate times before completing this section.

1. Have you tried stamping on the spot when feeling anxious? YES/NO

2. Did it help you to release some of your stress and anxiety? YES/NO

3. Did this strategy help you to feel less anxious? YES/NO

4. Are you adding this strategy to your Coping List? YES/NO

#60
5 THINGS YOU CAN SEE

If you can feel your anxiety becoming overwhelming or you are having an anxiety attack, then lots of people have success with the 54321 method. This method is a distraction technique and works by guiding your attention on to other things aside from your anxiety. To do this technique, you should firstly think of or say five things that you can see like "I can see a picture, a wall, a TV, a pen and a tree". Followed by four things you can touch like a ring on your hand, your phone, your hair or your jeans. Then three things you can hear like music, people talking or a TV. Then two things you can smell like some perfume or something in the fridge. Then one thing you can taste inside your mouth like what you had for lunch or saliva. If you can't hear, smell or taste anything then just move on to the next one and repeat this method until your anxiety has calmed down. Remember that you can walk around when you use this technique to find things to help distract you from your anxiety.

Try this strategy at least three separate times before completing this section.

1. Did this strategy help to distract your mind from your anxious thoughts? YES/NO

2. Were you able to find and think of things to distract your attention? YES/NO

3. Are you adding this strategy to your Coping List? YES/NO

#61
COUNTING NUMBERS

Counting numbers can help to distract our minds from anxious and intrusive thoughts. If you feel your anxiety building up, try and break the pattern of anxious thought by breathing mindfully and counting slowly to fifty. Once you have counted up to fifty, work your way back down, then up again, then down again, until you feel your anxiety subsiding.

Try this strategy at least three separate times before completing this section.

1. Did this strategy help to distract your mind from your anxious thoughts? YES/NO

2. Did you breathe mindfully while counting? YES/NO

3. Did this strategy help you to feel less anxious? YES/NO

4. Did it help you to avoid having a panic attack? YES/NO

5. Are you adding this strategy to your Coping List? YES/NO

#62
LEARN A POEM

Learning or reading a poem can have a calming effect on our minds as we distract ourselves by thinking about the words in the poem. Choose a poem that is either positive, funny, calming or offers a mixture of these feelings so that the poem impacts you in the right way. If you feel your anxiety becoming overwhelming, try and read or recite your poem to divert your attention away from your anxious feelings. If you feel comfortable or you are on your own, then say it out loud. If you are in a public space or somewhere you do not want to speak out loud then say it in your head. You may not know any poems at the moment, but there are thousands on the internet that you can enjoy reading through. Find the ones that resonate with you and use these to help you when you need them.

Try this strategy at least three separate times before completing this section.

1. Have you found poems to read or recite that are either positive, funny, calming or a mixture of these emotions? YES/NO

2. Did reading or reciting them help you to feel less anxious? YES/NO

3. Are you adding this strategy to your Coping List? YES/NO

#63
SING A SONG OUT LOUD OR IN YOUR HEAD

From the moment you wake up in the morning or as soon as you feel anxious thoughts trying to intrude into your head, sing a positive song that you love and makes you feel good. The song you sing should help you to overcome any negative thoughts, replacing them with positive and upbeat words and affirmations like 'I feel happy', 'I feel good', 'I feel strong' and so on. Songs that work well for this are James Brown's 'I Feel Good' and Nina Simone's 'Feeling Good', but there are a million others out there. So, either try these or find ones that suit you and you love to sing.

Try this strategy at least three separate times before completing this section.

1. Have you picked a song or songs to sing when you feel anxious thoughts creeping in? YES/NO

2. Which songs have you chosen?

3. Did singing them help to distract you from your anxious feelings? YES/NO

4. Did this strategy help you to feel less anxious? YES/NO

5. Did it help you to avoid having a panic attack? YES/NO

6. Are you adding this strategy to your Coping List? YES/NO

#64
STRESS BALLS AND FIDGET SPINNERS

Do you find yourself playing with your hands? Tapping a pen on your desk? Twirling your hair? Tapping your feet or just generally fidgeting? Well then, a fidget spinner or a stress ball or toy might be just the thing for you. Fidgeting or messing around is part of our body's natural response to feeling stressed and feeling bored and unfocused. By using one of these toys, you are providing yourself with a tool to direct your attention towards that is low energy and relaxing. Used for helping people with ADHD and autism, it can also be a useful tool for people who are trying to cope with feelings of anxiety and panic. Studies have shown that just by playing with these stress relievers they can help to decrease feelings of anxiety by up to 20%.

Try this strategy at least three separate times before completing this section.

1. Have you tried using these when you have felt anxious and you are fidgeting? YES/NO

2. Did it help you to feel less anxious and focus your attention? YES/NO

3. Are you adding this strategy to your Coping List? YES/NO

#65
PLAY WITH SILLY PUTTY

Just as playing with fidget spinners and stress balls can help to relieve symptoms of anxiety so can playing with silly putty. As you massage the silly putty through your fingers, you are focussing your concentration away from your anxiety and on to the task in hand. This meditative activity can help to encourage feelings of relaxation and lower your feelings of anxiety. For an added boost of tranquillity try adding Lavender oil to the silly putty and inhaling its vapours as you play with it.

Try this strategy at least three separate times before completing this section.

1. Have you tried playing with silly putty when you have felt anxious YES/NO

2. Did this strategy help to distract your mind from your anxious thoughts? YES/NO

3. Did you add Lavender oil to it? YES/NO

4. Are you adding this strategy to your Coping List? YES/NO

#66
SAY THE ALPHABET BACKWARDS

Another distraction technique you can try when feeling anxious is saying the alphabet backwards. This technique forces you to focus on the letters of the alphabet and distracts you away from your anxious and intrusive thoughts. To start with you may have to work your way up through the alphabet to get to the letter you need. However, with time you will be able to master saying it backwards. So, the next time you feel your anxiety building up or a panic attack setting in, try and use this technique to refocus your attention and calm yourself down.

Try this strategy at least three separate times before completing this section.

1. Did this strategy help to distract your mind from your anxious thoughts? YES/NO

2. Did this strategy help you to feel less anxious? YES/NO

3. Did it help you to avoid having a panic attack? YES/NO

4. Are you adding this strategy to your Coping List? YES/NO

#67
JUST DO SOMETHING/2-MINUTE RULE

If you are feeling anxious or you feel like a panic attack is coming on, do not just sit there and let it happen. Do something. Do anything. Take control. Whether that's practising a breathing technique, picking up this book to look at some tips, using a distraction technique, running your wrists under cold water, removing yourself from a situation, lying down and closing your eyes or something else. Just do something. Do not let anxiety take control of you; you take control of it. This may be tiring, especially as you embark on your journey of taking back control but practice makes perfect. An excellent way to do this is by following the 2-minute rule. This focusses on the maximum amount of time you should spend worrying about something. If you notice that you have been worrying about something for more than two minutes, then you need to get up and do something to distract you from your thoughts. You do not have to time yourself exactly, but if you feel like you have been sat or stood there worrying for too long, then you need to switch up your thought process by using one of the strategies in this book or by doing something else. Focussing on your anxious thoughts for too long is not productive for your mental health. So, make sure to recognise when you are doing this and implement the 2-minute rule.

---

1. Are you adding this strategy to your Coping List? YES/NO

#68
BUILD A WALL

When anxious thoughts enter your head, try building an imaginary wall in your mind that nothing can penetrate. As negative thoughts enter, let them bounce off your solid wall like a football bouncing off a brick wall. This may be difficult to imagine at first, but with practice, you should be able to master this. Once you have prevented the thoughts from entering your mind, try and refocus your attention on to something else. This could be speaking to someone, playing on your phone, drawing or something else.

Try this strategy at least three separate times before completing this section.

1. Were you able to build an imaginary wall in your head? YES/NO

2. If YES did this strategy help to distract your mind from your anxious thoughts? YES/NO

3. Did this strategy help you to feel less anxious? YES/NO

4. Did it help you to avoid having a panic attack? YES/NO

5. Are you adding this strategy to your Coping List? YES/NO

#69
COLD WATER

Splashing cold water slowly on your face or running cold water on your wrists can help you to feel less anxious when your anxiety is building up and also during an anxiety attack. This is because cold water helps to lower your heart rate and body temperature, which can increase as your anxiety becomes overwhelming. By keeping yourself cool, you can help to stabilise your anxiety levels. You can also try drinking a glass of cold water or putting a cool damp cloth on the back of your neck.

Try this strategy at least three separate times before completing this section.

1. Did you try splashing cold water on your face slowly? YES/NO

2. Did you try running cold water on your wrists? YES/NO

3. Did either of these strategies help you to feel less anxious? YES/NO

4. Did it help you to avoid having a panic attack? YES/NO

5. Are you adding this strategy to your Coping List? YES/NO

RELAXATION

The strategies and tips in this section will teach you relaxation techniques that will help you to manage your anxiety, its symptoms and feelings.

#70
478 BREATHING

Learning effective breathing techniques can have a significant and positive impact on your mental wellbeing. One of these techniques is 478 breathing. This strategy is easy to learn and can help you to regulate your breathing, making you feel calmer and less on edge. It can also help to lower your racing heart when you feel an anxiety or panic attack coming on. To try this strategy, breathe in through the nose for 4 seconds, hold your breath for 7 seconds, and then breathe out with force for 8 seconds. Repeat this technique four times or continue it until you feel calmer, or your panic has subsided. If you can close your eyes when using this breathing technique, then this will increase your opportunity to relax as you shut down the overwhelming sense of sight. The beauty of this technique is that you can do this anywhere, anytime, anyplace. If you can, try listening to relaxing music while completing this breathing technique to increase its effectiveness.

---

1. Did this strategy help you to feel relaxed and less anxious? YES/NO

2. Are you adding this strategy to your Coping List? YES/NO

#71
LISTEN TO RELAXING MUSIC

Make sure to take time out in your day to listen to relaxing music as studies have shown that listening to music like this can help to reduce anxiety by up to 65%. When you are anxious and stressed, you can feel uptight and tense. Thankfully, music can help to relax your body and mind and lower your anxious feelings. Have a relaxing CD or playlist ready at home, in your car or on your phone and listen to it at any opportunity you get. You can find relaxing music on YouTube and other streaming sites and its genres include classical music, specific anxiety relaxing music, world music and more. You can try listening to it on your way to and from work to help you to destress or when you are in the bath, on the couch or just during general everyday life.

---

1. Did this strategy help you to feel relaxed? YES/NO

2. Did this strategy help you to feel less anxious? YES/NO

3. What type of relaxing music did you listen to?

4. Are you adding this strategy to your Coping List? YES/NO

#72
FIND MOMENTS IN THE DAY TO RELAX

In this modern era, many of us live very pressured lives, and our minds are always on the go. Whether it's financial pressure, pressure from work, family, friends, partners, ex-partners or something else, the pressure is everywhere. This can all contribute to how anxious we are feeling, and so with this in mind; we must find time to relax our body and mind when we can. There are different ways we can do this, and it all depends on how much time you have to yourself in the day. If you have the time to lie down on your bed or sofa without being disturbed then do so. If you are always on the go, then you need to be smart about how you find times to relax. Instead of using your phone on the toilet, close your eyes and breathe mindfully for a couple of minutes. If you are commuting to work, try listening to relaxing music. Or if at home, try turning your phone and the TV off, closing your eyes and just enjoying the quietness for a few minutes. You can take these moments spontaneously or plan them into your day in advance. That could be relaxing in the bath, working out at a yoga class or any other way. Whatever it is, these moments will help your body to recharge and get some much-needed moments of relaxation in your pressured life.

---

1. Are you adding this strategy to your Coping List? YES/NO

#73
MEDITATE

Meditating is good for the soul and great for fighting anxiety. Whether you meditate for a minute, an hour or more, meditation can help us to break the cycle of constant anxious thoughts. It gives us some quiet time and relaxation in our day and can help us to become more in touch with our feelings. This can help us to address the root causes of our anxieties. The beauty of meditating is that you can do it anytime, anyplace, anywhere and if you are a complete newbie to it, then there is lots of information available online. There are also lots of videos on YouTube that will coach you through a variety of meditation techniques. Watch a few of them until you find one that you enjoy and works for you. Furthermore, there are also various breathing techniques in this book that will help you to meditate. However you do it; the wellbeing boosts that meditation can offer your anxiety is well worth channelling your inner Zen.

Try this strategy at least three separate times before completing this section.

1. Did this strategy help you to feel relaxed? YES/NO

2. Did this strategy help you to feel less anxious? YES/NO

3. Did you follow a YouTube video? If so, which ones?

4. Are you adding this strategy to your Coping List? YES/NO

#74
CLOSE YOUR EYES AND LIE DOWN

If your anxiety is becoming overwhelming or you can feel a panic attack coming on then sometimes the best thing to do is to find somewhere you can just close your eyes and lie down for a few minutes. By allowing yourself a moment's peace to relax and by removing the overwhelming sense of sight, you are allowing your anxiety to calm down. To help you relax further, you could try using one of the breathing strategies in this book or any other techniques that work for you. Maybe you can't lie down because you are at work, on the train or somewhere else? If this is the case, then go to the nearest toilet cubicle, sit down, close your eyes and just find a moments peace for a few minutes. These little moments of recuperation will help you to get through your day when you need them.

Try this strategy at least three separate times before completing this section.

1. Did this strategy help you to feel relaxed? YES/NO

2. Did this strategy help you to feel less anxious? YES/NO

3. Are you adding this strategy to your Coping List? YES/NO

#75
STRETCH YOUR BODY

If you are feeling anxious try and relax your body one area at a time through stretching. Standing up, work down from your head to your toes, starting by tilting your head side to side then back and forth, holding each motion for 5 seconds. Then roll your shoulders backwards and then forwards five times each way. Then stretch your arms out wide and then in again five times. Followed by rotating your hips one way and then the other, five times each way. Then keep your legs straight and touch the floor or as near as you can get to it and hold it for 5 seconds. Followed by tensing and then releasing your toes for 5 seconds. Repeat this process five times. By tensing and then releasing these areas of your body, you will help it to release the pent-up anxiety that is making you feel tense. It may be that you are familiar with lots more stretches than the ones here, so feel free to incorporate them into this activity. If you are not used to stretching, then there is lots more information available online that will help you to get the most out of this activity. Try and do this every morning to kickstart your day or every evening to help you relax before you go to bed.

---

1. Did this strategy help you to feel relaxed and less anxious? YES/NO

2. Are you adding this strategy to your Coping List? YES/NO

#76
HUG SOMEONE

One thing we should all be doing is hugging more. Studies have shown that hugging someone for just 20 seconds can lead to our bodies releasing a hormone called oxytocin. This 'cuddle hormone' as it is also known can help to play a role in lowering your blood pressure, slowing your heart rate down and improving your mood. Therefore, if you are feeling anxious or you are experiencing an anxiety or panic attack, maybe it's time to get hugging. Hopefully you have someone to hug, if so, make sure to hug them for at least 20 seconds every day. Free hugs anyone?

1. Did this strategy help you to feel relaxed? YES/NO

2. Did this strategy help you to feel less anxious? YES/NO

3. Did it help you to avoid having a panic attack? YES/NO

4. Are you adding this strategy to your Coping List? YES/NO

#77
BLOW BUBBLES

Sounds fun and childish. Well, that's because it is. However, blowing bubbles slowly can help us to relieve stress and anxiety as we regulate our breathing and concentrate on blowing bubbles and not on our anxious thoughts. When we feel anxious one of the things we should do to help us is focus mindfully on our breathing. When blowing bubbles, that is exactly what we are doing without realising it. We breathe in deeply and then slowly breath out as we try and form the bubbles. As we do that we are also concentrating on the formation of the bubbles and not on our anxious or intrusive thoughts. We then get to enjoy them floating through the air and gently popping which can be relaxing in itself. If you think about it all, it makes sense. You can do this indoors or if the sun is shining go outside, get some vitamin D and watch as your bubbles float through the air. So, what are you waiting for? Get on Amazon, order some bubbles and get bubbly.

---

1. Did this strategy help you to feel relaxed? YES/NO

2. Did this strategy help you to feel less anxious? YES/NO

3. Are you adding this strategy to your Coping List? YES/NO

#78
USE A COLOURING BOOK

Colouring books for adults have proven to be extremely popular in recent years with studies suggesting that their use can have various benefits for your mental health. It is suggested that the concentration used when colouring can help to induce a meditative state and reduce the symptoms of depression and anxiety. It has also been shown to increase mindfulness. So, if you are feeling anxious now or the next time you do, maybe take some time out, get the colouring books and crayons out and colour the day away.

Try this strategy at least three separate times before completing this section.

1. Did this strategy help you to feel relaxed? YES/NO

2. Did this strategy help you to feel less anxious? YES/NO

3. Did it help you to avoid having a panic attack? YES/NO

4. Are you adding this strategy to your Coping List? YES/NO

#79
DO PUZZLES OR A SUDOKU

Studies have shown that completing puzzles and games like Sudoku can have a positive effect on our mental health and help to decrease feelings of anxiety. It has been suggested that when completing these games, we feel like we have achieved something and find this rewarding. This can help us to fight any negative feelings that might creep their way into our day. Along with enjoying these mini triumphs in what might be an otherwise stressful day, these puzzles also help to provide our brain with a workout, improving and maintaining its function. So, it looks like it might be worth getting the puzzles and Sudoku out on the bus, on the toilet, on the couch or anywhere else for that matter and taking time out of the day to get those mini wins in your life.

Try this strategy at least three separate times before completing this section.

1. Did this strategy help you to feel relaxed? YES/NO

2. Did this strategy help you to feel less anxious? YES/NO

3. Are you adding this strategy to your Coping List? YES/NO

#80
TAKE A POWER NAP

Something that you probably already know and that studies have shown is that not getting enough sleep can have a detrimental effect on your mental health, triggering anxiety and feelings of confusion and fatigue. Just one bad night's sleep can have a damaging impact on how we feel and several bad nights just piles up the misery. If you are struggling to get the recommended 7 to 8 hours a night sleep due to insomnia, work, children or for any other reason then try and take naps in the day. Sometimes this is easier said than done, but further studies have shown that just 20 minutes of power napping can help to improve our mood, performance and alertness. So, the next time someone calls you lazy or asks why you are closing your eyes in the middle of the day, remind them that it is for the benefit of your mental health and nothing is more important than having good health. Please note, do not nap too late as this will affect your night-time sleep pattern.

---

1. Are you getting enough sleep at night? YES/NO

2. Have you tried taking 20-minute power naps? YES/NO

3. Did this strategy help you to feel less anxious? YES/NO

4. Are you adding this strategy to your Coping List? YES/NO

#81
PLAY WITH A PET

Studies have shown that being around animals can have a positive effect on our mental health. They can help to lower stress levels, anxiety and isolation while also improving our mood. If you have a pet then spending time stroking them and cuddling them can also help to increase your levels of oxytocin which is known as the cuddle hormone. This promotes feelings of love and relaxation while decreasing your levels of cortisol and pain. Furthermore, dog owners also benefit from walking their pets which provides both exercise and opportunities to walk outside and be in nature, all of which have a positive effect on anxiety. So, if you haven't got a pet, and your situation allows it, it might be time to think about getting a little furry friend. And if you can't have a pet for whatever reason, then you can always visit your local animal rescue centre where you will be able to walk their dogs and cuddle their cats.

1. Does spending time with animals help you to feel less anxious? YES/NO

2. Are you adding this strategy to your Coping List? YES/NO

#82
TAKE UP A HOBBY

Taking up a hobby can have lots of positive impacts on your life and helping your mental health is one of them. It can help to alleviate stress and anxiety by giving you something to focus on that you enjoy doing while helping to calm your overactive mind. This helps to fulfil your soul with a sense of achievement while also providing you with an experience that distracts you from anxious and negative thoughts. Hobbies can include cooking, writing, working out, yoga, painting, pottery, dog walking, sports, knitting, drawing or anything else that you enjoy. If you have a hobby that you enjoy doing already then that's great, keep it up. But if you haven't found one just yet, then there are lots of groups out there for all abilities and videos and courses online if you want to try something at home.

---

1. Do you have a hobby? YES/NO

2. What is it?

3. How does your hobby make you feel?

4. If you haven't got a hobby, what would you like to do?

5. Are you going to continue or start taking up a hobby? YES/NO

6. Are you adding this strategy to your Coping List? YES/NO

#83
DRAW A PICTURE OR PATTERNS

Drawing can help to relieve symptoms of anxiety by calming our nervous system as our concentrated mind induces a state of mindfulness and relaxation. This can help to lower our blood pressure, regulate our breathing and bring our heart rate to a more relaxed tempo. Drawing anything can be beneficial, but drawing patterns can further help to encourage these feelings as the movement of your pen or pencil becomes hypnotic. This is a great stress-relieving activity which can help to break up the day and allow you to escape your anxiety for a little while.

Try this strategy at least three separate times before completing this section.

1. Have you tried drawing a picture or patterns when you feel anxious? YES/NO

2. Did this strategy help you to feel relaxed? YES/NO

3. Did this strategy help you to feel less anxious? YES/NO

4. Did it help you to avoid having a panic attack? YES/NO

5. Are you adding this strategy to your Coping List? YES/NO

#84
HOLD HANDS

Along with hugging, holding hands with someone is suggested to release oxytocin which as mentioned previously is a chemical responsible for helping us to feel relaxed and loved. Studies have shown that this simple act can have pain-relieving qualities that help to reduce anxiety. Moreover, any caring human contact, be that with your partner, your kids or any other family member contributes to boosting your soul and easing your symptoms of anxiety. So, being affectionate with those you love should never be underestimated, especially where anxiety is concerned.

---

1. Do you get enough caring human contact in your life? YES/NO

2. Are there people you can share caring human contact with? YES/NO

3. Who can you hold hands with?

4. How does holding hands make you feel?

5. Did this strategy help you to feel less anxious? YES/NO

6. Are you adding this strategy to your Coping List? YES/NO

#85
SOUNDS OF NATURE

Like relaxing music, studies have shown that listening to the sounds of nature can help our bodies to relax. It can decrease our levels of anxiety and lower our levels of the stress hormone cortisol. The next time you feel anxious try walking in the garden, in the park or somewhere peaceful and listen to the sounds of the birds, the bees and the breeze. Alternatively, there are several apps available that will play sounds of nature, and there are also playlists available on YouTube and other streaming services. Whether you are at home, work or somewhere else, the next time you feel your anxiety rising above unmanageable levels try closing your eyes, breathing mindfully and listening to the sounds of nature.

Try this strategy at least three separate times before completing this section.

1. Did this strategy help you to feel relaxed? YES/NO

2. Did this strategy help you to feel less anxious? YES/NO

3. Are you adding this strategy to your Coping List? YES/NO

#86
4X4 BREATHING

4X4 breathing or box breathing as it is also known as is a breathing technique that can help you to relax when you are feeling anxious or stressed. This technique is often used by the military, sports stars and celebrities because it induces relaxation while improving performance and focus. To try this method, you should firstly breathe in through your nose for 4 seconds filling your lungs from the bottom to the top. Then you should hold this breath in for 4 seconds before slowly breathing out for 4 seconds. Then hold your exhaled breath for 4 seconds. You should complete this process four times, and as you get better at it, you can increase the seconds you breathe in, out and hold for. This technique will help you to reset your breath when you are feeling anxious and you can feel your symptoms bubbling up.

1. Did this strategy help you to feel relaxed? YES/NO

2. Did this strategy help you to feel less anxious? YES/NO

3. Did it help you to avoid having a panic attack? YES/NO

4. Have you tried this technique to help you fall asleep? YES/NO

5. Are you adding this strategy to your Coping List? YES/NO

#87
PEEL AN ORANGE

Peeling an orange and inhaling the aromas of citrus is suggested to have a positive effect on our anxiety. Keep a bowl of oranges in the kitchen or at work and the next time you feel your anxiety becoming overwhelming, reach for the fruit bowl, unravel the peel and inhale its citrusy aromas. To get even more creative you can try making orange peel potpourri, or you can simmer the peel in a small pan of boiling water and fill your kitchen with the smell of oranges.

1. Did this strategy help you to feel relaxed? YES/NO

2. Did this strategy help you to feel less anxious? YES/NO

3. Are you adding this strategy to your Coping List? YES/NO

#88
ALTERNATE NOSTRIL BREATHING

Another breathing technique you can try to relieve your anxiety is Alternate Nostril Breathing or Nadi Shodhana (channel purification) as yoga lovers may call it. This slow breathing technique does exactly what it says on the tin and concentrates on breathing in and out through one nostril and then in and out through the other. To practice this technique, you should close one of your nostrils using your thumb. You should then breath in through your open nostril for 4 seconds and then out through the same nostril for 4 seconds. Once completed, you should close the alternate nostril with your thumb and then breath in through your open nostril for 4 seconds and then out again for 4 seconds. You should repeat this process for at least a minute, or more as you get used to doing it. This is a fast-acting technique that can help to relieve anxiety quickly, calming your senses and giving you an energy boost when you need it.

---

1. Did this strategy help you to feel relaxed? YES/NO

2. Did this strategy help you to feel less anxious? YES/NO

3. Did it help you to avoid having a panic attack? YES/NO

4. Are you adding this strategy to your Coping List? YES/NO

#89
PRACTICE MINDFULNESS

Mindfulness seems to be such a buzz word nowadays and for a good reason. It is the process in which we focus our attention on our own experiences and feelings within the present moment and without judging them good or bad. In being mindful, we can identify our feelings and behaviours, which allows us opportunities to work on them as part of a broader picture. We can practice being mindful or mindfully meditating by just sitting in silence and with no distractions for a few minutes. Focus on your breathing using one of the breathing techniques in this book and think about how you have been feeling and how you have been behaving. Try and allow yourself to become familiar with your anxious thoughts without becoming scared by them or judging them good or bad. This will enable you to address your anxiety more calmly. You can either sit or lie in silence or you can mindfully meditate while walking, practising yoga, drawing, colouring or through another relaxing practice.

1. Did this strategy help you to feel relaxed? YES/NO

2. How did you practice being mindful? What did you do?

3. Did this strategy help you to feel less anxious? YES/NO

4. Are you adding this strategy to your Coping List? YES/NO

#90
PLAN A BREAK OR HOLIDAY

Sometimes you just need a break. A little bit of time out, a holiday or a change of scenery can often do us a world of good. If you can financially afford it, book yourself some time away somewhere that you have always wanted to go. If money is an obstacle at the moment, try and escape to the local countryside or to the nearest coastal walk or beach. This much needed time out and relaxation can provide your body and mind with a break in your regular routine, allowing you the space to gather your thoughts. While on your break or holiday, try meditating mindfully and remember that there are positive and fun experiences to be had in life also.

---

1. Have you booked a break or day away? YES/NO

2. Where are you going?

3. If you haven't booked or arranged something, where could you go?

4. How does going on holidays and breaks make you feel?

5. Are you going to make more of an effort to enjoy a day or more somewhere relaxing? YES/NO

6. Are you adding this strategy to your Coping List? YES/NO

#91
TAKE A WARM BATH OR SHOWER

Have you ever got into your shower or bath and just said "Ahhhhhhh!". That's because a warm bath or shower can help our muscles and bodies to relax, which in turn can help to relieve feelings of anxiety. You should also try using relaxing bath salts and lighting candles while playing some calming music to enhance the tranquillity in your bathroom. Try adding this into your nightly routine and making it a relaxing part of your day. However, be careful not to have the water too hot as this can spike your body temperature too quickly, leading to an increase in feelings of anxiety.

1. Did this strategy help you to feel relaxed? YES/NO

2. Did this strategy help you to feel less anxious? YES/NO

3. Did you use bath salts? YES/NO

4. Did you light candles and listen to relaxing music? YES/NO

5. Are you adding this strategy to your Coping List? YES/NO

#92
SLOW DOWN

In this modern and fast-paced world, we often get caught up doing this and that, and we forget just to slow down. If you are feeling anxious it's time to stop rushing about, stop trying to please everyone, stop putting yourself under pressure and just slow down. Your mental health is so important to you, so stop rushing around. Remember working, keeping up with the Jones's, chasing the latest and greatest things and documenting it all on social media are not the most important things in your life. Try and take little moments in the day to just relax and mindfully breathe. Whether that's in the car, at home, on the toilet, in work or somewhere else. Just slow down, close your eyes and enjoy moments of tranquillity.

---

1. Do you lead a busy life? YES/NO

2. Do you find yourself trying to do things all the time?

3. On self-reflection, do you think you need to start finding times to slow down? YES/NO

4. Where and when can you find moments in your day to relax?

5. Are you going to start relaxing in these moments? YES/NO

6. Are you adding this strategy to your Coping List? YES/NO

#93
READ A BOOK

Studies have suggested that just ten minutes of reading your favourite book can help to reduce your levels of anxiety and stress as you focus your concentration on the story you are engaged with. This is because as you continue to read more, your breathing becomes regulated, your body and muscles relax, and your heart rate steadies. Interestingly, studies have actually shown that reading can help to reduce stress by over 60%, which is great when you realise that you are benefitting from doing something that you enjoy. If you aren't an avid reader, it might just be time to put your phone down and delve into a good old book.

---

1. Do you read regularly? YES/NO

2. If NO, are you going to start? YES/NO

3. Does reading help you to feel more relaxed? YES/NO

4. If YES, are you going to try and read every day or at least regularly? YES/NO

5. Are you adding this strategy to your Coping List? YES/NO

#94
BLOW ON YOUR THUMB

Sounds crazy, right? Well apparently, blowing on your thumb can help to relieve your anxiety and it's all down to something called your vagus nerve. This nerve runs parallel to your brainstem and into your chest and stomach. Studies have shown that stimulating it can help you to feel more relaxed by lowering your blood pressure and heart rate. To try this technique, put your thumb in your mouth up to the bottom of your fingernail and purse your lips together. Inhale through your nose for 4 seconds, hold it in for 4 seconds and then with your thumb still in your mouth, exhale through your mouth for 7 seconds. Repeat this four times or until you feel less anxious. One of the reasons that this is believed to work is because our thumbs have a strong pulse, and it is connected to our vagus nerve. As we blow on it, it triggers our vagus nerve to slow down our heart rate and blood pressure, thus lowering feelings of anxiety. So, blowing on your thumb to help improve your anxiety might not be quite as crazy as it seems.

Try this strategy at least three separate times before completing this section.

1. Did this strategy help you to feel relaxed? YES/NO

2. Did this strategy help you to feel less anxious? YES/NO

3. Are you adding this strategy to your Coping List? YES/NO

#95
ACUPRESSURE

A form of traditional Chinese medicine, acupressure is said to have anxiety-relieving qualities. By applying pressure to certain areas of the body, including your head, ears, shoulders, hands, wrists and feet, this technique is said to help relieve stress and pressure within our bodies. If you can financially afford to then find a local practitioner who can perform this practice for you. If you would prefer to save your money then there are plenty of videos on YouTube for you to watch and try on yourself. Or you could always ask a family member or friend to help.

Try this strategy at least three separate times before completing this section.

1. Did this strategy help you to feel relaxed? YES/NO

2. Did you find someone to do it for you or did you do it yourself?

3. Did this strategy help you to feel less anxious? YES/NO

4. Did it help you to avoid having a panic attack? YES/NO

5. Are you adding this strategy to your Coping List? YES/NO

#96
MASSAGE

Let's face it. Everyone loves a massage. Why? Because it's super relaxing and that's exactly what we need when we are filled with anxiety. Massages have lots of benefits for our body and mind, including helping to reduce tension while working to lower our levels of the stress hormone cortisol. Along with these benefits, massages can also help us to improve our circulation and flexibility while steadying our heart rate and blood pressure. Studies have shown that people who receive massages regularly over time will see a decrease in their anxiety and symptoms of anxiety. So, if you can financially afford to go to a spa then get yourself booked in ASAP. However, if you would prefer to save the pennies try asking your partner, family member or friend if they would give you a massage as it's going to benefit your mental health.

1. Did this strategy help you to feel relaxed? YES/NO

2. Who did you get to massage you?

3. Did this strategy help you to feel less anxious? YES/NO

4. Are you adding this strategy to your Coping List? YES/NO

#97
RELAX YOUR BODY FROM HEAD TO TOE

Anxiety can make our bodies feel tense, so it is essential to release that tension whenever we can. An excellent way to do this is by relaxing our bodies from head to toe. When lying on your back or sat comfortably, relax every part of your body area by area. If it helps to listen to some soothing music while you are doing this, then do so, or you can just enjoy the silence. As you carry out this destressing technique focus on your breathing and try teaming it up with one of the breathing techniques in this book. To start relaxing your body, focus your thoughts on your toes, tensing them slightly and releasing them. You can tense all of your toes at the same time or concentrate on one foot and then the other. After this, focus on the soles of your feet, thinking about them becoming relaxed. Then your shins and calves. Then your thighs and quads. Followed by your hips, bum, stomach, lower back, upper back, chest and neck. Then work your way down your arms towards your fingers. Then tense your fingers, then let them go. Then work back up your arms to your neck. Then your chin, your cheeks, your mouth and jaw. Followed by your eyes and nose and finally your head. Do not rush this process and take at least 20 seconds focussing on each area. If you fall asleep during this process, then that's great. Just enjoy the peacefulness as your mind and body relax you to a more tranquil state. Repeat the process if needed.

1. Are you adding this strategy to your Coping List? YES/NO

#98
YOGA

Yoga is an ancient Indian form of exercise and practice that is great for the mind, body and soul. Having been around for over 5,000 years, it is now probably as popular globally as it has ever been. Focusing on breathing, strength and flexibility yoga can be practiced anywhere in the world; the gym, your office, the garden, your living room, a beach, or anywhere else you can imagine. You can practice yoga at no cost to yourself, without anyone watching and it's amazing for your body and your anxiety. It's win-win. In practising yoga, you are training your mind and taking control of your body, teaching it to become healthy and also how to relax. As you become more mindful of your breathing, yoga will help to lower your heart rate and blood pressure. It will also lower the levels of cortisol in your body, which is the body's natural stress hormone. There will be classes you can go to locally, or if you would rather do it in your own home, then there are lots of videos on YouTube and books available to teach you. This is something anyone can do, from beginners to yoga gurus – just give it a try and see how you feel.

1. Did this strategy help you to feel relaxed? YES/NO

2. Did you enjoy yoga? YES/NO

3. Did yoga help you to feel less anxious? YES/NO

4. Are you adding this strategy to your Coping List? YES/NO

#99
PILATES

Pilates is a more modern form of exercise when compared to yoga; however, like yoga, it has positive benefits for the mind, body and soul. Focussing on breathing, strength and flexibility Pilates can be practiced anywhere from the home to the office to the gym. Like yoga and other forms of exercise, there will be local Pilates classes in your neighbourhood that you can take part in. If you would rather do it in your own home, then you can get books from the library or Amazon or use YouTube to follow Pilates videos. The benefits of Pilates for anxiety are that it helps to encourage relaxation and mindfulness, lowering the levels of cortisol (stress hormone) in your body while enhancing your levels of serotonin. It can also help to reduce your heart rate and blood pressure while relaxing and strengthening the muscles in your body. Have a look at both yoga and Pilates and see which one suits you best. You may want to do both or focus on one or the other?

---

1. Did this strategy help you to feel relaxed? YES/NO

2. Did you enjoy Pilates? YES/NO

3. Did Pilates help you to feel less anxious? YES/NO

4. Are you adding this strategy to your Coping List? YES/NO

#100
WEIGHTED BLANKETS

Weighted blankets are a favourite for anxiety sufferers with studies suggesting they can help you to relax and get a good night's sleep. Weighing between 5 and 30 pounds, weighted blankets can have an earthing effect which makes your body feel like it's being pushed towards the ground. This deep pressure stimulation is said to relieve symptoms of anxiety while lowering the levels of cortisol (stress hormone) in your body. Costing from 20 pounds/dollars or euros to hundreds of pounds/dollars or euros on sites like eBay and Amazon, there are blankets to suit all budgets. If you are looking for something to help you relax on the sofa or get a better night's sleep, then this might be a good option for you.

---

1. Have you bought a weighted blanket? YES/NO

2. Did this strategy help you to feel relaxed? YES/NO

3. Did this strategy help you to feel less anxious? YES/NO

4. Did this strategy help you to sleep better? YES/NO

5. Are you adding this strategy to your Coping List? YES/NO

#101
PUT YOUR FEET UP

Something we all love to do at the end of a hard day is to put our feet up and relax. However, did you know that by doing so, you can help to relieve your anxious feelings? By elevating your feet higher than your head and your heart, your bodies circulation takes the pressure away from your legs and feet and helps to calm your nervous system down. There is a yoga pose named after this called Viparita Karani which involves you lying on the floor with your legs up the wall. Try holding this position for a couple of minutes or until you feel less anxious. Not only can this help you to feel calmer, but it can also help your body become more rebalanced if you have been standing or sitting all day. If this pose is too difficult, then try lying on your sofa, putting cushions on the arms of the sofa and propping your feet up on top of them.

1. Did this strategy help you to feel relaxed? YES/NO

2. Did you do the Viparita Karani pose or did you put your feet up on the sofa?

3. Did this strategy help you to feel less anxious? YES/NO

4. Are you adding this strategy to your Coping List? YES/NO

#102
ASMR

Something that has grown in popularity in recent years with millions upon millions of views on YouTube is Autonomous Sensory Meridian Response or ASMR for short. Some of you will be familiar with ASMR, and some of you will be thinking what on earth is that? Well for those of you who have never heard of it before, in its purest form it is video or audio stimulus that can make you experience low and sometimes high levels of euphoria. If triggered correctly, it can make you feel a tingling sensation in your head, neck, back and sometimes down your body. Or for some people it can just make them feel pleasant. For those ASMR works for it can be a great relaxant and can help to ease your anxiety, stress, depression and insomnia. If you would like to try listening to some ASMR videos then just head to YouTube and type in ASMR. There are thousands of videos with male and females' voices and different sounds to choose from, so try a few until you find the ones that work for you. You might also want to try these with headphones in to get an even closer experience.

---

1. Did this strategy help you to feel relaxed? YES/NO

2. Did this strategy help you to feel less anxious? YES/NO

3. Are you adding this strategy to your Coping List? YES/NO

#103
FLOTATION THERAPY

A form of therapy that has been popular since the 1970s and used by celebrities and athletes alike is flotation therapy. This involves entering a flotation tank (or isolation tank/sensory deprivation tank as it is also known) and just floating. The tank is filled with water and a high concentration of Epsom salts. This enables the human body to just float on top of the water without the fear of drowning. In this modern age, we experience sensory overload daily, but flotation tanks allow you to enter an environment where your senses of touch, smell, sound and sight are significantly reduced. This is suggested to have a deep physical and mental effect on your body and mind helping you to reach high levels of relaxation, relieve pain and most importantly in the context of this book, relieve anxiety. Please note though that depending on your relationship with your anxiety, being deprived of your senses may fill you with even more anxiety and panic. However, if it does sound like something you would like to try and there is a flotation centre close to your location, then it is worth looking into.

1. Have you tried flotation therapy? YES/NO

2. Did this strategy help you to feel less anxious? YES/NO

3. Are you adding this strategy to your Coping List? YES/NO

PROFESSIONAL HELP

The strategies and tips in this section will provide you with some options of professional help that is available to you and can help with your anxiety.

#104
SEE A DOCTOR

It sounds so simple, but if you feel like you need to speak to your doctor about how you are feeling, then reach out to them. You will not be the first person they have talked to about anxiety, and you certainly won't be the last. Your doctor will be able to advise you on what you can do to help yourself and also advise you on what help is available to you. They will be able to do things like refer you on to specialist services, prescribe you with medication and offer you the support you need on your journey with anxiety. Reach out to them.

---

1. Have you spoken to your doctor about your anxiety? YES/NO

2. What was the outcome of this?

3. How did this make you feel?

4. Will you continue to speak to your doctor about your anxiety? YES/NO

5. Are you adding this strategy to your Coping List? YES/NO

#105
SEE A THERAPIST

Talking to your friends and family and trying the techniques in this book might be helping you, which is great. But sometimes you might need a little more help, and if so, it could be time to call a specialist in. A therapist or counsellor might help you to make more sense of your thoughts and feelings and give you more in-depth techniques to cope with how you feel. There are lots of techniques and practices that counsellors and therapists can work with you on like Cognitive behavioural therapy (CBT). This is a tried and tested method to change the way you think and behave. If you Google 'anxiety therapist' or 'anxiety counsellor' then there will be lots of people who come up in your local area who can help you. If you can't afford to see a therapist straight away, then you can usually access these services through the national health service. There will be long waiting lists, but eventually, you will get to speak to someone. There are also charitable organisations who might be able to help with counselling services. Please see the back of this book for more details on them. However, if you do have some money available, it might be time to prioritise your spending. Is it better to pay for a night out drinking, a new pair of jeans, cigarettes or a sports bet? Or is the money better spent on helping to mend your mind?

---

1. Are you adding this strategy to your Coping List? YES/NO

#106
MEDICATION

Sometimes we all need a little extra help with our anxiety, and there is no shame in admitting that. If a medication helps to improve how you feel, then using it is not a weakness. Try the techniques in this book first, and if you are still struggling and in crisis, then see a therapist or speak to your doctor about starting a course of anti-anxiety medication. However, remember that you do not have to be on medication forever. Once you have built up your coping strategies, like the ones in this book, then you can slowly wean yourself off again if you wish. One thing to keep in mind, no matter how desperate you feel, never buy fake or illegal anxiety medication off the internet. You do not know what ingredients are in them, and it could be anything, even fatal. If this is the route you are looking at, it is far more sensible and safer to speak to your doctor and ask them for prescribed medication.

1. Have you spoken to your doctor about the medications available to you? YES/NO

2. Are you taking medication for your anxiety? YES/NO

3. Do you want to learn other strategies to cope with your anxiety? YES/NO

4. Are you adding this strategy to your Coping List? YES/NO

#107
CBT

CBT or Cognitive behavioural therapy as it is also known is a form of psychotherapy treatment that can help you with your anxiety. There are several areas that CBT looks at and helps you to make sense of, including your thoughts, the physical feelings you get, the emotions you feel, the situations you might be in and the actions you take. CBT looks at all of these areas with the view that they are interconnected and helps you to identify what makes you anxious, your response to it and how you can resolve this. CBT can take the form of one to one sessions with a therapist or health worker, in a group or as part of an online session or course. However you access CBT, it will help you to understand your anxiety and provide you with coping strategies that could help you to overcome your feelings and symptoms. CBT will not work for everyone who has anxiety, but it does have a high success rate for helping people suffering from anxious feelings. If you would like to explore CBT, then do your research on the internet or in the library and speak to your doctor about accessing your local services.

---

1. Does CBT sound like something you would like to try? YES/NO

2. Have you tried CBT before? YES/NO

3. Did it help you to manage your anxiety? YES/NO

4. Are you adding this strategy to your Coping List? YES/NO

#108
HYPNOTHERAPY

Hypnotherapy is a form of alternative therapy in which a patient is encouraged to act or feel a certain way following a process called hypnosis. Somebody who carries out these treatments is called a hypnotherapist, and there are lots of reasons someone might want to see one. Hypnotherapists can help a variety of people including those who are suffering from phobias, people who would like to give up drugs, alcohol or smoking, people with PTSD and people who are stressed, depressed and anxious amongst other things. During a hypnotherapy session, a hypnotherapist will help to guide you to a deep state of relaxation and concentration where they will help you to see and address the problems in your life. Studies have shown that hypnotherapy can be hugely successful in helping people with anxiety problems. So, it may be worthwhile looking on Google and seeing if there is an excellent practitioner available in your local area.

---

1. Have you seen a hypnotherapist? YES/NO

2. Did working with them help you to feel less anxious? YES/NO

3. If you haven't seen a hypnotherapist yet, are you going to? YES/NO

4. Are you adding this strategy to your Coping List? YES/NO

FEEL GOOD

The strategies and tips in this section will teach you techniques that will help you to feel good despite your anxious feelings.

#109
READ OR BE TOLD JOKES

Remember the old saying 'laughter is the best medicine'? Well, it could well be true. Studies have shown that laughing triggers the release of endorphins which are known as the body's natural feel-good chemicals and also act as a natural pain relief. It is also shown to increase infection-fighting antibodies while lowering stress hormones like cortisol. With that in mind if you are feeling anxious ask a friend, family member or work colleague to tell you their best or worst jokes. If there is no one around to tell you jokes, then get your phone out and look for the top 100 funniest jokes on Google or whatever jokes will make you laugh the most.

---

1. Did you ask someone to tell you jokes? YES/NO

2. Did you read jokes? YES/NO

3. Did either of these help you to improve your mood? YES/NO

4. Are you adding this strategy to your Coping List? YES/NO

#110
MAKE YOURSELF SMILE

Did you know that smiling can trick your brain into feeling happy? Well, now, you do. Scientific studies have shown that a simple smile can kickstart a powerful chemical reaction in your brain, releasing the hormones dopamine and serotonin. These are both linked to lowering stress levels and increasing happiness. With this in mind, try smiling ten times, holding each smile for 10 seconds at a time to help boost your mood and feelings.

Try this strategy at least three separate times before completing this section.

1. Did it help you to feel happier? YES/NO

2. Did it help you to feel more relaxed? YES/NO

3. Are you adding this strategy to your Coping List? YES/NO

#111
GO OUTSIDE AND INTO NATURE

Feeling stressed and anxious? If so, it is time to head back to nature to unwind. A relaxing walk in the countryside, on the beach or in a similar setting can help to relax your soul while giving your body a positive chemical boosting exercise. If you can, try and plan daily or at least weekly walks, into your life and stick to your plans. If you struggle to get outside, try and bring the outdoors in by creating an indoor nature garden made up of anti-anxiety plants like Aloe Vera and Rosemary. Not only will your indoor garden offer you a sense of nature. It will also provide you with something to focus your attention on and take a sense of ownership over.

---

1. Did you go for a walk somewhere scenic and relaxing? YES/NO

2. Did it help you to feel good? YES/NO

3. Where did you go?

4. Have you created an indoor garden? YES/NO

5. Does creating and maintaining this help you to relax and feel good? YES/NO

6. What plants did you use?

7. Are you adding either of these strategies to your Coping List? YES/NO

#112
VOLUNTEER IN THE COMMUNITY

Wondering why this is here? Well if you have the time and you need to build your confidence up within social environments then try volunteering within the community. This can be as simple as helping a neighbour out by getting their shopping, walking dogs at an animal sanctuary, helping out in a local food bank or something else. By volunteering not only are you breaking formed patterns in your anxiety, you are also creating a feel-good factor in an otherwise anxious life. There are lots of people who volunteer who have physical or mental health problems, may be lonely or may have other limiting factors in their life. With this in mind, you will likely find a non-judging environment in which you can build your social skills and confidence up again.

1. Have you tried volunteering in the community? YES/NO

2. Where did you volunteer?

3. Did you feel good doing so? YES/NO

4. Will you continue to volunteer in the community? YES/NO

5. Are you adding this strategy to your Coping List? YES/NO

#113
SELF-CARE

In this modern and crazy world, it is essential to take a step back and to make time for yourself. If your finances will allow you to, then go for a massage, get your hair, nails, beard, teeth, or whatever you want worked on. It's important to feel good, and we often feel good when we are relaxed and look good. This will not solve the root cause of your anxiety but it might help you to feel a lot better than you have been recently. It's also worth noting that finding things that make you feel good in an otherwise anxious life are worth doing. On the flip side if you haven't got a lot of money but would still like to treat yourself, then research local colleges that offer beauty therapy courses. There will often be students who are looking for clients to train with who they can offer these services for free or little cost. Do not become obsessive over this as that is not what we are aiming for, instead treat yourself to a little pampering now and again.

---

1. Have you been for any self-care treatments? YES/NO

2. What did you do?

3. Did it make you feel good? YES/NO

4. Will you keep treating yourself? YES/NO

5. Are you adding this strategy to your Coping List? YES/NO

#114
WATCH SOMETHING FUNNY

As mentioned previously laughing is known as the body's natural feel-good chemicals. It helps to release endorphins that lower stress and promotes all-round positive mental health and wellbeing. With that in mind, it's time to ditch the serial killer boxsets, conspiracy theories and the deep space mind-boggling documentaries and start watching things that make you laugh. Whether that be a funny film, a sitcom or even a Disney film, it's time to start tuning in to more light-hearted television. If you find yourself out of the house and away from the TV you can always turn to YouTube. There you can find a million and one things that could make you laugh, from silly things that animals do to the top twenty epic fails. Helping your anxiety and stress while watching something that makes you laugh is a winning combination.

Try watching only funny films, sitcoms and compilations for a day, couple of days or week.

1. Have you tried this strategy? What did you watch?

2. Did it make you laugh and improve your mood? YES/NO

3. Did you feel relaxed and less anxious while watching it? YES/NO

4. Are you adding this strategy to your Coping List? YES/NO

#115
DANCE TO MUSIC

From those of you who can move like Fred Astaire to those who are more 'can't dance but don't care', dancing is something that lots of people love to do wherever they are in the world. Whether it's dancing alone in the house or shaking your thing amongst a club full of people, dancing can be great fun. The best thing of all is that it can also have a positive effect on your mental health as it helps to lower stress and boost your levels of serotonin. Along with helping you to feel good, it can also help to distract your mind as you lose your concentration into the music and away from harmful and intrusive thoughts. As if that wasn't enough, it can also help to provide you with an aerobic exercise which can further boost your serotonin levels while helping to regulate your breathing. So, if you are feeling anxious it might be time to hit play on your favourite records and dance like nobody is watching.

1. Have you tried dancing when feeling anxious? YES/NO

2. Did dancing help to improve your mood and feel good? YES/NO

3. Did dancing help to distract your mind from anxious thoughts? YES/NO

4. Are you adding this strategy to your Coping List? YES/NO

#116
FAITH & SPIRITUALITY

This suggestion might not suit everyone as not everybody believes in a higher power or is spiritual. However, for those of you that do you may find that praying or talking to your God or being in touch with your spirituality can help you to manage your stress and anxiety. Studies have suggested that praying can help to relieve some anxious feelings however this does depend on the God you are praying to and the personality you deem them to have. Are they helpful and forgiving or are they mean and nasty? You may not believe in a God or maybe haven't thought about it before? However, you certainly have nothing to lose if you decide to pray, talk to a higher power or get in touch with your spiritual side.

1. Did talking to a higher power help you to feel better about your anxiety? YES/NO

2. Did it help you to feel less anxious? YES/NO

3. Did it help you to feel more relaxed? YES/NO

4. Are you adding this strategy to your Coping List? YES/NO

#117
ENJOY THE SUNSHINE

Whether you live in the sunniest of cities or the rainiest of villages, we should all be seeking the sun wherever we can as it can be extremely beneficial for our mental health. Without looking at the science straight away and just going off your feelings and experiences, how do you feel when it is raining and miserable outside compared to how you feel when the sun is shining? I'm guessing you prefer it when the sun is shining, right? That's because we associate the sun with good times and memories and because exposure to it increases our levels of the feel-good hormone serotonin. It also boosts our levels of vitamin D, which a deficiency in (as explained in another section) can lead to symptoms of anxiety. Furthermore, sunny days can also encourage us to be more active outside and seek adventures to beaches, parks, the countryside and similar settings. All of which help to boost our wellbeing. So, if you live somewhere sunny make sure to make the most of it. Moreover, if you live somewhere rainy, when the sunny days do come along don't just sit indoors feeling anxious, get out there and feel the warm sun on your skin.

---

1. Are you adding this strategy to your Coping List? YES/NO

THINGS TO LIMIT

The strategies and tips in this section will look at things that you should limit. This is because they could be a trigger of your anxious symptoms and feelings and make your anxiety worse.

#118
ALCOHOL

I know this isn't what you want to hear, and I am genuinely sorry, but as you probably already know alcohol is the devil when it comes to anxiety. It might alleviate your symptoms while drinking it, deleting the nervousness from your life and turning you into captain confidence. However, overall, it has a negative impact on your brain. It alters your levels of serotonin and disturbs your neurotransmitters which can lead to an increase in anxious feelings once the relaxing effects of alcohol wear off. Its hangovers can lead to dehydration, an unbalanced brain, low blood sugars and an increased heart rate. All a melting pot of nasties for anyone who already suffers from anxiety. The odd glass of wine or pint here or there isn't going to send you into an anxious oblivion but stay away from binge drinking. There will be many people, maybe even you, who use alcohol as a coping mechanism, especially within social circles. If you must go hard or go home, then try drinking pints of water in between your alcoholic drinks. This will help you to keep hydrated and prevent you from drinking too much alcohol. It is also worth thinking about how you behave when you are drunk as you may act a certain way and say and do things that will make you feel more anxious once you are sober.

---

1. Are you adding this strategy to your Coping List? YES/NO

#119
SMOKING

Studies have shown that in the long-term smoking can increase anxious feelings as opposed to being a relaxant as many people believe. Although nicotine does create a sense of relaxation in the short term, once this initial feeling has passed this soon leaves way to an increase in cravings and withdrawal symptoms. These body-altering feelings can often leave smokers feeling on edge and anxious if they have not had a cigarette. It's better never to start, but if you do smoke it's time to think about ditching the cigarettes as there is more than just your lungs and other physical organs at risk. There is lots of help out there to stop smoking, but giving up is easier said than done. Good luck.

---

1. Are you a smoker? YES/NO

2. If YES do you feel more anxious if you have not had a cigarette or smoke? YES/NO

3. Do you want to give up smoking? YES/NO

4. Are you going to give up smoking? YES/NO

5. Are you adding this strategy to your Coping List? YES/NO

#120
AVOID ILLEGAL DRUGS

Taking illegal drugs, whether once or more, can have a damaging effect on your mental health. The types of drugs taken and the length of time they have been taken for, all play a role in how your mental health and wellbeing will feel. Some drugs can make you feel anxious while using them and others can make you feel anxious for days, weeks, months and years afterwards. The various types of illegal drugs widely available include Cocaine, Heroin, Spice, Ecstasy, Speed and even body enhancing drugs like steroids and fat burners. However, there are many more illegal drugs out there than listed here. Now, although illegal drugs may make people feel great in the present moment, often enhancing social environments, in the long run, they can have a detrimental effect on your health. If you are reading this, it is likely that you already have anxiety, in which case stay clear of any illegal drugs as your mental health is already compromised and they will not help you in any way. If you do not have anxiety take this as a stark warning; taking illegal drugs can significantly affect your mental health in many ways and is not worth the risk in the long term. Now it is true that not everyone who takes illegal drugs will develop mental health problems. However, the link between them has been proven time and time again.

---

1. Are you adding this strategy to your Coping List?
   YES/NO

#121
CAFFEINE

Caffeine is a powerful stimulant and should be treated as such by those with anxiety. It is one of those triggers you are probably aware of but don't want to admit, especially for those of you who love a daily coffee or ten. Caffeine can stimulate our body's natural flight or fight response, which can make your anxiety feel worse and even trigger an anxiety attack. You might not want to hear this, but it might be time to give up that much-loved cup of coffee that helps you to get through the day! Shock! Horror! Although anxiety can often leave you feeling tired, reaching for a coffee might not be the answer as they contain high levels of caffeine. Other products that are high in caffeine include full sugar cola's and other similar soft beverages, dark chocolate, tea, and some medications. If you love the taste of coffee or tea and can't imagine giving them up, then you could try opting for caffeine-free alternatives instead. Of course, not everyone with anxiety will be negatively affected by caffeine. Still, it is worth monitoring as it can have an impact on how you feel.

This is something to observe on an ongoing basis.

1. Have you noticed that some foods and drinks high in caffeine can make you feel more anxious after consuming them? YES/NO

2. Are you adding this strategy to your Coping List? YES/NO

#122
ENERGY DRINKS

Just like with coffee, we can often find ourselves reaching for energy drinks when we are feeling tired and fatigued. However, although this seems like the right thing to do, just like drinking coffee, it is the wrong thing to do for people who suffer from anxiety. Energy drinks are absolutely packed to the rafters with caffeine, which in large amounts is a big no-no if you want to keep your body calm and relaxed. These high levels of caffeine can lead to you feeling more anxious, jittery and even trigger a full-blown panic attack. For those of you who are partial to vodka on a night out you should also avoid coupling this up with energy drinks. Alcohol has a negative effect on anxiety anyway but partnered with energy drinks; then it becomes double trouble. Although you might feel fantastic and full of life while intoxicated your body has the potential to fall out with you later on in the night and most definitely the next day.

---

1. Do you usually drink energy drinks? YES/NO

2. Have you noticed that energy drinks can make you feel jittery or anxious after drinking them? YES/NO

3. Are you adding this strategy to your Coping List? YES/NO

#123
WATCHING THE NEWS

Now it is good to know what's going on in the world and it's useful and sometimes needed to keep informed. However, in this super connected modern age, we are at risk of news overload, and this can affect our anxiety. When we are continually listening, reading and watching the news about illnesses, viruses, deaths, wars, violence, hate, crimes and so on, this can become overwhelming and play havoc with our already anxious minds. Being aware of things is good, but having fear and sadness pumped into your brains every day is not productive for someone with anxiety. If you can, try avoiding the news entirely for a couple of days and see how you feel. If you need to know what's going on in the world, watch, read or listen to the news just once a day. Do not absorb it in the evening and especially not when relaxing in bed. If you find yourself looking at news apps on your phone, delete them or only look at them once a day if you can keep disciplined. Another thing to be mindful of is that social media platforms can also be full of news, from people talking about it to news organisations and businesses sharing information. With this in mind, it might be useful to take a social media break or limit your time on there, if you find that negative news adds to your anxiety.

---

1. Does the news add to your anxiety? YES/NO

2. Are you adding this strategy to your Coping List? YES/NO

#124
TURN YOUR PHONE OFF

As mentioned previously, we all live in a super-connected world where everything we want to know is at our fingertips. People can get hold of us any time they need to and vice versa. This can be great sometimes, but not all the time. Like social media, it is a blessing and a curse. If you are feeling overwhelmed by technology, it might be time to take a break from your phone. Turn it off and just enjoy some peace and allow your mind to power off as your phone powers off. Sit in silence for 30 minutes and just relax. If you find yourself always on it in an evening, try buying a lockable box that you can put your phone into when at home. Then if you feel things are getting too much, remove the technology from your life, lock your phone away and just allow yourself to relax. Remember it's great and positive to stay connected, but it doesn't have to be 24/7.

---

1. Are you always using your phone? YES/NO

2. Do you feel like you need to take breaks from using your phone? YES/NO

3. Are you going to start turning your phone off and taking breaks from using it? YES/NO

4. Are you adding this strategy to your Coping List? YES/NO

#125
TAKE A SOCIAL MEDIA BREAK

Everyone loves a bit of social media, but sometimes it can become overwhelming, and our brains and eyes need a rest from the screen and from comparing our lives to other peoples. In comparing our lives with 'picture perfect' images and stories, we can create negative feelings about our own lives which can create feelings of anxiety and inadequacy. Do not let this happen. If you feel this way, then you need to take a social media break until you feel confident, at ease and happy in yourself. Make sure to stay connected to people in whatever ways suit you but don't overuse social media and don't compare yourself to others through it. Everybody's story is different.

---

1. Do you use social media? YES/NO

2. Do you use social media too much? YES/NO

3. Do you find yourself negatively comparing your life to other peoples? YES/NO

4. Are you going to take a break from social media? YES/NO

5. If you have taken a break from social media, how did this make you feel?

6. Are you adding this strategy to your Coping List? YES/NO

DIET AND NUTRITION

The strategies and tips in this section will look at how what you eat and drink can impact your anxiety positively and negatively.

#126
PROCESSED SUGAR

As much as everyone loves foods packed with processed sugar, they can have a negative impact on your anxiety levels. Foods and drinks that are brimming with processed sugar include chocolate, cakes, sweets, fizzy drinks, fruit juices, biscuits, some yoghurts, some kinds of ketchup, sweet and sour sauce and many more. The list is vast, but if you pay attention to what you are consuming, you will soon be able to identify these anxiety enabling culprits quickly. So why is processed sugar so bad for people suffering from anxiety? Well, what goes up must come down, and sugary highs can make you come crashing down to shaky lows. This can lead to you feeling tense and irritable, which are all side effects that can make your anxiety feel worse. This is because sugar affects your blood sugar levels, fluctuating them, and making your body work extra hard to maintain its normal levels. If you suffer from anxiety, this rush of ups and downs can leave you feeling even more nervous and drained. It isn't the primary cause of anxiety, but it can make symptoms feel a lot worse. If you have a sweet tooth and need to satisfy the urge, try making a fresh fruit salad with pineapple and strawberries or Google some healthier alternatives instead.

Keep notes and monitor how you feel after consuming foods and drinks high in processed sugar.

1. Are you adding this strategy to your Coping List? YES/NO

#127
EAT ANXIETY FIGHTING FOODS

Now while it's important to avoid trigger foods that enable your anxiety, at the other end of the spectrum, there are foods that have anti-anxiety qualities. If you are looking towards your diet to improve how you feel, then studies have shown that Brazil nuts, fatty fish, eggs, pumpkin seeds, turmeric, Chamomile, yoghurt, green tea, and almonds are all worth adding to your shopping list. What you eat and how often you eat can all play a vital role in how anxious you feel, so it is essential to eat the right foods and avoid the wrong foods. It is worth doing your research around foods that help to combat anxiety as you need to find the ones that are appealing to you and your lifestyle.

1. Have you tried any of the anxiety fighting foods mentioned? YES/NO

2. Did you enjoy any of the anxiety fighting foods, and if so, which ones?

3. Will you be adding these into your daily diet? YES/NO

4. Have you found any other anxiety fighting foods that you like? YES/NO

5. Will you be adding eating anxiety fighting foods to your Coping List? YES/NO

#128
ANTI-ANXIETY COOKBOOKS

As described in this book, there are lots of foods that can trigger anxiety, but there are also lots of foods that can have a positive effect on your mental health. Trying to work out what to eat can be quite overwhelming, but as with most things, help is at hand. Luckily for you, there are lots of anti-anxiety cookbooks available that have lots of yummy recipes from the simple to the sublime. Whether you are looking for foods that boost your immune system, mellow your mood or help you to avoid trigger foods, there are lots of delicious dishes out there. To find them just visit Amazon Books and type in Anxiety Cookbooks, then buy whichever ones look the most suitable.

---

1. Have you bought any anti-anxiety cookbooks? YES/NO

2. Have you made any of the recipes? YES/NO

3. Which recipes did you make?

4. If you eat anti-anxiety foods, do they help you to feel healthy? YES/NO

5. Are you adding this strategy to your Coping List? YES/NO

#129
EAT MEALS REGULARLY

As many anxiety sufferers will know too well, our bodies can be extremely sensitive, reacting to slight changes in extreme ways. That is why it is essential to eat healthy balanced meals regularly to keep your blood sugar levels stabilised. If your blood sugar levels are not stabilised, then they can make your body feel like it is going through a sugary roller-coaster with great highs and shaky, nervous lows. Skipping just one meal or waiting too long between meals can cause your blood sugar levels to drop, which can result in a nasty cocktail of anxious symptoms. This for someone already suffering from anxiety is not a good place to be. So, make sure to eat the right kinds of foods and at the correct times of day by planning and preparing your meals and mealtimes.

1. Do you eat regular and nutritious meals at the right times of the day? YES/NO

2. Do you often skip meals or wait too long between meals? YES/NO

3. Have you noticed that missing meals can make your anxiety worse? YES/NO

4. Are you going to plan your meals and snacks daily? YES/NO

5. Are you adding this strategy to your Coping List? YES/NO

#130
HAVE A RECOVERY PACK OF FOOD

As described in this book, you need to eat healthy meals regularly to maintain your blood sugar levels. With this in mind, you should always have a recovery pack of food available to you. Whether this is at home, at work, when travelling or when out and about. Anxiety can make you feel fatigued, so it's vital to have energy-rich foods available to you as and when you need them. Bananas are a cheap and awesome source of energy, rich in tryptophan which is an amino acid responsible for inducing serotonin and relaxation in our bodies. If you don't like bananas, then oranges are also a great snack to turn to in your recovery pack. They boast high levels of vitamin C, which helps to improve our immune systems and its citrusy aromas have a calming effect on our mind and body. These amazing snacks are cheap and full of goodness but feel free to find your own that you like.

---

1. Do you often skip meals or wait too long between meals? YES/NO

2. Are you going to start carrying snacks around with you? YES/NO

3. Which snacks will you choose?

4. Are you adding this strategy to your Coping List? YES/NO

#131
ALMONDS

Almonds are a great and natural source of vitamin E, and magnesium, which studies have shown have anti-anxiety qualities. Add to this the fact that they have been shown to help stabilise blood sugars and you have an anxiety fighting superfood. You can try adding almonds into your day by swapping your morning milk for almond milk, or you can try eating them raw or as some supermarkets offer them, roasted or salted.

1. Have you tried eating almonds? YES/NO

2. Do you like almonds? YES/NO

3. Are you going to add almonds to your daily diet? YES/NO

4. Are you adding this strategy to your Coping List? YES/NO

#132
BROCCOLI AND CELERY

Broccoli and celery are both a natural source of Potassium, and Folic Acid, which studies have shown have anti-anxiety qualities. Having a Potassium or Folic Acid deficiency is shown to be a cause of anxious feelings and symptoms, so by eating the right foods, you will help to keep your body in balance. This will not affect everyone, but it will not harm you to get a daily or weekly dose of some healthy greens and keep your vitamin and mineral levels topped up.

1. Have you tried broccoli and celery? YES/NO

2. Do you like broccoli and celery? YES/NO

3. Are you going to add broccoli and celery to your daily diet? YES/NO

4. Are you adding this strategy to your Coping List? YES/NO

#133
VITAMIN D DEFICIENCY

Low levels of vitamin D can lead to you feeling tired, fatigued, have aches and pains and feel depressed. All of these symptoms are also associated with anxiety, so it may be worth asking a doctor to check your vitamin D Levels. In the UK alone, it is thought that 1 in 5 people have a vitamin D deficiency, which is more prevalent in the winter as there are lower levels of sunlight there. Foods that are naturally rich in vitamin D include egg yolks, mushrooms, fatty fish like salmon and tuna, cod liver oil, fortified cereals and some cheeses like goats' cheese and ricotta cheese. If you feel like your vitamin D Levels might be low then the only way to check for this is through a blood test with your local doctor, health service or by using an online provider. If you find out that your vitamin D levels are low, then your doctor will likely prescribe you vitamin D supplements and suggest for you to eat more of the foods that are listed above.

1. Have you had your vitamin D levels tested? YES/NO

2. Do you have low levels of vitamin D? YES/NO

3. Are you taking vitamin D supplements and adding vitamin D rich foods to your diet? YES/NO

4. Are you adding this strategy to your Coping List? YES/NO

#134
LACTOSE INTOLERANCE

Being lactose intolerant has absolutely nothing to do with your foot missing some of its toes. What it does mean is that your bodies digestive system reacts negatively when you consume a type of sugar (lactose) found in cow's milk and dairy. It is thought that 1 in 5 people in the UK might be lactose intolerant and in the USA, it is 1 in 3, with African Americans, Asian Americans and American Indians having intolerance levels as high as 75%-90% of their population. If you are lactose intolerant you will likely have an upset stomach, bloating, gas and nausea following consuming dairy. If you do have any of these symptoms and find that the consumption of milk and dairy correlates with your levels of anxiety, then it might be worth asking your doctor for a test or buying a testing kit online. If you think lactose may be affecting your anxiety, try keeping a food journal and tracking how you feel after you have consumed milk and dairy.

---

1. Have you noticed that consuming cow's milk or dairy products can leave you feeling more anxious afterwards? YES/NO

2. Are you lactose intolerant? YES/NO

3. Are you adding this strategy to your Coping List? YES/NO

#135
GLUTEN INTOLERANCE

Being gluten sensitive or intolerant means that your body has an adverse reaction to you eating wheat, barley and rye. At its worst it can lead to an autoimmune disease that can affect your gut and/or your brain. If it affects your gut, this is known as celiac disease, and if it affects your brain, this is known as ataxia. In the UK, around 1 in every 100 people are gluten intolerant with many going undiagnosed for years. Some may never be diagnosed at all. Having a gluten intolerance can have obvious symptoms; however, it can also be asymptomatic meaning it has no symptoms. In the case of this book, having a gluten intolerance has been shown to cause anxiety and anxious feelings in people. So, it may be worthwhile asking your doctor for a blood test to see if the gluten you are consuming is affecting your anxiety. If you do think gluten may be affecting your anxiety try keeping a food journal. That way, you can track how you feel after you have consumed gluten-containing foods like bread, pasta, cakes, pizza and more.

---

1. Have you noticed that consuming gluten containing foods can leave you feeling more anxious afterwards? YES/NO

2. Are you gluten sensitive? YES/NO

3. Are you adding this strategy to your Coping List? YES/NO

#136
HYDRATE

Sounds simple right? Well, in coping with your anxiety, you need to make sure that your body stays hydrated throughout the day. Studies have shown that when our body is dehydrated, it does not function as well as it should. Blood pressure may drop, which can lead to dizziness and a faster heartbeat as the heart tries to increase low blood pressure. This can all lead to bringing on a panic attack, so make sure to stay hydrated. Carry a water bottle around with you throughout the day and if you do not like drinking water all the time, try adding diluting juice to it.

1. Are you drinking enough water or liquid throughout the day? YES/NO

2. If YES great, if not, are you going to try and drink more water or liquid throughout the day? YES/NO

3. Have you noticed that you feel more anxious if you need a drink or don't have a drink with you? YES/NO

4. Do you always carry a drink around with you where possible? YES/NO

5. Are you adding this strategy to your Coping List? YES/NO

#137
AVOID OR LIMIT FRUIT JUICES

There are various fruits that have anti-anxiety qualities and eating raw fruit is great for you. However, once the fruit has been blended up, it turns natural sugars into free sugars, and free sugars are bad for the body. They can affect your anxiety as they fluctuate your blood sugar levels, causing panic-like symptoms and nervousness. Now, a glass of freshly squeezed fruit juice a day isn't going to ruin your world, but as with anything, everything in moderation. Overdo it, and it may start to have a negative effect on your anxiety. Instead, why not try swapping fruit juice for something like an apple and a glass of water.

1. Do you drink fruit juice? YES/NO

2. Have you noticed that if you drink a lot of fruit juice you can feel more anxious afterwards? YES/NO

3. Are you going to avoid or limit drinking fruit juices? YES/NO

4. Are you adding this strategy to your Coping List? YES/NO

#138
AVOID FIZZY DRINKS WITH SUGAR

Fizzy drinks like cola, orangeade and lemonade are full of sugars that can affect your blood sugar levels and cause symptoms of anxiety. Like fruit juices, they can have a negative effect on your anxiety as they fluctuate your blood sugar levels, causing nervousness and panic attacks. You should aim to avoid drinking these types of fizzy drinks but if you must have them, then choose diet drinks with no added sugars.

1. Do you drink fizzy drinks with sugar in? YES/NO

2. Have you noticed that if you drink a lot of these types of drinks, you can feel more anxious afterwards? YES/NO

3. Are you going to avoid or limit drinking these drinks? YES/NO

4. Will you choose to drink diet drinks instead of drinking these drinks? YES/NO

5. Are you adding this strategy to your Coping List? YES/NO

HOW TECHNOLOGY
CAN HELP

The strategies and tips in this section will look at how technology can help you to cope with your anxiety.

#139
SMART PHONE APPS

If you have a smartphone, then there are lots of apps that can help you when you are feeling stressed, when you feel anxious and when you can't sleep. These include Calm, Happify, Dare, Headspace, breathing apps like Wim Hof Method and Breathwrk, various meditation apps, nature sound apps, mindfulness apps, exercise apps, cooking apps and much more. Download and try them all and see which ones work well for you and your anxiety.

1. Have you downloaded some phone apps to help you with your anxiety? YES/NO

2. Which apps did you download?

3. Did they help you to feel less anxious or help you with your anxiety strategies? YES/NO

4. Are you going to download more apps? YES/NO

5. Are you adding this strategy to your Coping List? YES/NO

#140
PHONE GAMES

If you need a quick distraction technique from feeling anxious and your usual strategies are letting you down, then you could try playing games on your phone. Yeah, that's right, sounds fun, doesn't it? If you have a smartphone, then there are lots of repetitive games available that can capture your concentration and require little effort. Download some games for your phone, and if you start to feel anxious or negative thoughts start to creep in then open up a game and focus on that instead. Try playing it for a little while or at least until your anxiety has begun to subside. If you do use this strategy try not to become addicted to any games, especially those that require payment or continued payments as this can add to your anxiety and is counterproductive. Just choose something simple, free and fun and remember it's something you can turn to wherever you are.

---

1. Have you downloaded some games on your phone? YES/NO

2. Have you tried playing games when you have felt anxious? YES/NO

3. Did they help you to feel more relaxed and less anxious? YES/NO

4. Are you adding this strategy to your Coping List? YES/NO

#141
COLOURING APPS

Just as colouring and drawing in books can help to lower our feelings of anxiety so can using colouring apps on our phone. Sometimes colouring books and crayons might not be to hand, but our phones will be. If this is the case, try an app like Colorfly, which is an extremely popular app for colouring in a variety of patterns, including animals and famous paintings. This fun activity can help to refocus your attention, regulate your breathing and relax your mind and body. Apps like these are straightforward, and you do not have to be Vincent Van Gogh to use this strategy.

---

1. Have you downloaded a colouring app? YES/NO

2. Have you tried using it? YES/NO

3. Did it help you to feel relaxed? YES/NO

4. Did it help you to feel less anxious? YES/NO

5. Are you adding this strategy to your Coping List? YES/NO

#142
CRANIAL ELECTROTHERAPY
STIMULATION

Relatively unknown by the average person on the street and relatively high in price, a cranial electrotherapy stimulation (CES) device may offer you some relief from your anxiety and any pains and stress that you may have. The device delivers small and natural micro-currents to specific nerves in your brain. This is said to encourage the stimulation of alpha brain waves which studies have suggested can help to relieve anxiety. It all sounds very technical, right? Well do your research and if it looks like something you might want to try then the option is out there. A popular brand is Alpha-Stim but there are others available also.

---

1. Have you bought a CES device? YES/NO

2. Has it helped to improve your anxiety? YES/NO

3. Will you keep using it? YES/NO

4. Are you adding this strategy to your Coping List? YES/NO

#143
DO AN ONLINE COURSE

One of the great things about living in this era of technology is that we have information available to us quickly and at the press of a button. With that in mind, it might be worth looking into doing an online course that covers anxiety and panic disorders. There are lots of courses available online, some of which are free and some of which are paid for. These courses will give you an insight into anxiety and panic. They will educate you on various topics from the science to the symptoms, from behaviours to coping strategies and more. Knowledge is power, and in learning about anxiety and panic, you will be better equipped to accept it and cope with it. Just by typing in 'anxiety online course' into Google's search bar, you will find lots of different options available to you from paid courses on educational sites like Udemy to free courses on sites like Future Learn. If you do decide that this is for you then happy learning.

1. Have you signed up to any online courses? YES/NO

2. If so which ones?

3. Have you completed any online learning courses? YES/NO

4. Did they help you to understand your anxiety? YES/NO

5. Are you adding this strategy to your Coping List? YES/NO

NATURAL PRODUCTS

The strategies and tips in this section will look at how natural products can help you to cope with your anxiety.

#144
ROSE OIL

Rose oil is suggested to have anxiety-relieving qualities and is known for helping with high stress, grief, and depression. Try putting some in a diffuser when you are relaxing in your house at night and inhale its scents. You can also try adding Rose oil to a warm bath and enjoying a long relaxing soak in its aromas.

---

1. Have you tried using Rose oil in a diffuser? YES/NO

2. Have you tried using Rose oil in your bath? YES/NO

3. If YES to any of the above, did Rose oil help you to feel relaxed? YES/NO

4. If YES to any of the above, did Rose oil help you to feel less anxious? YES/NO

5. Are you adding this strategy to your Coping List? YES/NO

#145
LAVENDER

Another homeopathic remedy that studies have shown can help to relieve anxiety and stress is Lavender. A beautiful smelling purple flower, Lavender is proposed to have a calming effect on the body, positively interacting with the brain and nervous system to settle feelings of anxiety and nervousness. The most popular way to reap the benefits of Lavender is by using it as an oil. You can try adding Lavender oils to your bath in the evening or by using it as an essential oil in a diffuser and inhaling its relaxing aromas. Alternatively, you can also try placing Lavender petals under your pillow before you go to bed at night. If you would like to use it in the day you could rub your phone, phone case, or watch strap with Lavender oil every morning, smelling it when you start to feel anxious.

1. Have you tried adding Lavender oil to your bath or burning it in a diffuser? YES/NO

2. Have you tried placing Lavender petals under your pillow at night? YES/NO

3. Have you tried rubbing your phone/phone case/watch strap with Lavender oil? YES/NO

4. Did any of these strategies help you to feel more relaxed and less anxious? YES/NO

5. Are you adding this strategy to your Coping List? YES/NO

#146
CHAMOMILE

There are various homeopathic remedies that studies have suggested can have a positive effect on some symptoms of anxiety. One of these is the Chamomile plant. Research has shown that ingesting Chamomile can help to promote relaxation and relieve anxiety and stress. If you would like to try Chamomile as a natural option to help alleviate your anxiety, then you can purchase Chamomile supplements or Chamomile tea. If choosing Chamomile tea, you can use readymade teabags or Chamomile flowers. These can all be bought online, from health stores and some supermarkets. You can also try using body products where Chamomile is the main ingredient or try using Chamomile oil in a diffuser at home. There is more scientific support for its anti-anxiety benefits when ingesting it as opposed to using body products and oils. However, feel free to try them all and see how they make you feel.

1. Have you tried Chamomile tea? YES/NO

2. Did drinking it help you to feel more relaxed and less anxious? YES/NO

3. Have you tried any other Chamomile products? If so, how did these make you feel?

4. Are you adding this strategy to your Coping List? YES/NO

#147
VALERIAN

Valerian is a herb that has a mild soothing effect on the body and can help with insomnia and anxiety. Used to treat people since the ancient Greek and Roman times, it is now widely available through health shops and over the internet. A popular homeopathic remedy, Valerian, is said to relax the body and help you to get a better night's sleep, which can be a welcome relief for those who struggle at bedtime. You can enjoy the reported benefits of it by taking a Valerian root supplement daily. But as with any supplement, please consult your doctor first as you may experience side effects. Although it can have benefits and is an over the counter remedy, it is always worth consulting a medical practitioner first. You can also try using Valerian oils, which depending upon its type, can be used in a diffuser to inhale or as a topic for your body.

1. Have you tried taking a Valerian root supplement? YES/NO

2. Did it help you to feel less anxious? YES/NO

3. Did it help you to fall asleep at night? YES/NO

4. Have you tried any other Valerian products? If so, how did these make you feel?

5. Are you adding this strategy to your Coping List? YES/NO

#148
CBD

Cannabidiol or CBD as it is better known has appeared everywhere in recent years and with good reason. Scientific studies and regular users have suggested that using it can assist in managing the different symptoms of anxiety. It's thought that this is because CBD interacts with receptors found in the nervous system, specifically the CB1 and CB2 receptors. This is said to have a beneficial effect for many ailments with anxiety being one of them. CBD can be bought in a variety of forms including flowers or buds, oils, capsules, skin products and more and can be found in health stores and online. If it sounds like something you might be interested in trying then do your research and give it a try.

1. Have you tried CBD? YES/NO
2. Which CBD products did you try?
3. Did it help you to feel more relaxed? YES/NO
4. Did it help you to feel less anxious? YES/NO
5. Are you adding this strategy to your Coping List? YES/NO

#149
EUCALYPTUS

Used for hundreds of years to treat a variety of ailments, including aches and pains, Eucalyptus is also suggested to have benefits for those suffering from anxiety. Studies have shown that it can help to reduce stress and feelings of anxiousness as it interacts with your nervous system creating a positive response. There are many ways in which you can use Eucalyptus. These include in the form of tea, topicals and by using its oils in a diffuser. A couple of other ways you can use Eucalyptus is by adding its leaves to your bath or by hanging them from your shower head and enjoying the warm and relaxing waters while the aroma of Eucalyptus fills the bathroom.

1. Have you tried using Eucalyptus? YES/NO

2. Did it help you to feel more relaxed? YES/NO

3. Did it help you to feel less anxious? YES/NO

4. Are you adding this strategy to your Coping List? YES/NO

#150
EPSOM SALTS

A completely different mineral to both your everyday table salt and sea salt, Epsom salts have been reported to have a positive impact on those suffering from stress and anxiety. The reason behind this is that Epsom salts contain sulphate and magnesium as opposed to sodium chloride, which is in both table salt and sea salt. It is the magnesium in Epsom salts that makes it super special though as researchers have shown that magnesium plays a role in the production of serotonin, the happy hormone. Having low levels of magnesium in our bodies can equal low levels of serotonin and feeling generally down. For someone with anxiety, it is essential to keep your serotonin levels as high as possible so that you can fight off low mood as you cope with your anxious feelings. A couple of ways in which you can enjoy the suggested benefits of Epsom salts are through flotation therapy as outlined in this book or by adding them to your evening bath. If you would like to add them to your evening bath, then there are lots of products available both online and in health stores. Please note that there have been reports that this is not suitable for people with diabetes. So, if this affects you, please consult your doctor before trying it. Otherwise, happy soaking.

---

1. Did using Epsom salts help you to feel more relaxed and less anxious? YES/NO

2. Are you adding this strategy to your Coping List? YES/NO

CONCLUSION

As you reach the end of this book, I hope you feel like you have learned new strategies and tips that can help to improve and change your life for the better. There will be tips and techniques that have worked amazingly for you. Then some that didn't work quite so well. The beauty of it is that everyone's anxiety coping mechanisms will be unique to them and their lives, as will yours. Similarly, your triggers will be unique to you, so understand them and put plans in place to avoid, limit or manage them appropriately. As terrifying as anxiety can be, I hope you have learned to accept it and not to be overly fearful of it. You are stronger than you know and I hope the tips in this book have helped you to realise this. Remember, today there may be clouds, but tomorrow there could be Sun. Always strive for the Sun and remember, positive mental health is wealth.

I would love to hear your feedback and hear about the tips that have worked well for you. If you would like to share your journey with me, you can contact me via email at hello@forhelpwithanxiety.com or by following me on Facebook by liking 'For Help with Anxiety', and on Instagram at @forhelpwithanxiety.

If you enjoyed the book and it helped you on your journey, please do leave a positive review on Amazon, so that other people who are experiencing the same feelings as you can see the value in it.

Take care, good luck on your journey and remember your 'Help with Anxiety' book is only ever a page turn away.

Best wishes, Ged

SUPPORT
ORGANISATIONS

All information is correct at the time of publishing:

United Kingdom

Hub of Hope

A national mental health database, bringing help and support together in one place. You can use this website to find services and organisations local to you by typing in your postcode.

Website: www.hubofhope.co.uk

Anxiety UK

Charity providing support if you have been diagnosed with an anxiety condition.

Phone: 03444 775 774 (Monday to Friday, 9.30 am to 5.30 pm)

Website: www.anxietyuk.org.uk

CALM

CALM is the Campaign Against Living Miserably, for men aged 15 to 35.

Phone: 0800 58 58 58 (daily, 5pm to midnight)

Website: www.thecalmzone.net

Men's Health Forum

24/7 stress support for men by text, chat and email.

Website: www.menshealthforum.org.uk

Mental Health Foundation

Provides information and support for anyone with mental health problems.

Website: www.mentalhealth.org.uk

Mind

Promotes the views and needs of people with mental health problems.

Phone: 0300 123 3393 (Monday to Friday, 9 am to 6 pm)

Website: www.mind.org.uk

No Panic

Voluntary charity offering support for sufferers of panic attacks and obsessive-compulsive disorder (OCD). Offers a course to help overcome your phobia or OCD.

Phone: 0844 967 4848 (daily, 10am to 10pm)

Website: www.nopanic.org.uk

OCD Action

Support for people with OCD. Includes information on treatment and online resources.

Phone: 0845 390 6232 (Monday to Friday, 9.30 am to 5 pm)

Website: www.ocdaction.org.uk

OCD UK

A charity run by people with OCD, for people with OCD. Includes facts, news and treatments.

Phone: 0845 120 3778 (Monday to Friday, 9 am to 5 pm)

Website: www.ocduk.org

PAPYRUS

Young suicide prevention society.

Phone: HOPElineUK 0800 068 4141 (Monday to Friday, 10 am to 5 pm and 7 pm to 10 pm, and 2 pm to 5 pm on weekends)

Website: www.papyrus-uk.org

Rethink Mental Illness

Support and advice for people living with mental illness.

Phone: 0300 5000 927 (Monday to Friday, 9.30 am to 4 pm)

Website: www.rethink.org

Samaritans

Confidential support for people experiencing feelings of distress or despair.

Phone: 116 123 (free 24-hour helpline)

Website: www.samaritans.org.uk

SANE

Emotional support, information and guidance for people affected by mental illness, their families and carers.

SANEline: 0300 304 7000 (daily, 4.30 pm to 10.30 pm)

Textcare: comfort and care via text message, sent when the person needs it most: www.sane.org.uk/textcare

Peer support forum: www.sane.org.uk/supportforum

Website: www.sane.org.uk/support

YoungMinds

Information on child and adolescent mental health. Services for parents and professionals.

Phone: Parents' helpline 0808 802 5544 (Monday to Friday, 9.30 am to 4 pm)

Website: www.youngminds.org.uk

REPUBLIC OF IRELAND

The Samaritans

Confidential support for people experiencing feelings of distress or despair.

Tel: 116 123

Website: www.samaritans.ie

Aware (Depression & Bi-Polar Disorder)

Aware provides support & information for people who experience depression or bipolar disorder and their concerned loved ones.

Tel: 1800 80 48 48

Website: www.aware.ie

Pieta House (Suicide & Self-harm)

National Suicide Helpline (Pieta House) 1800 247 247.

Tel: 01623 5606

Website: www.pieta.ie

Grow (Mental Health support and Recovery)

A national community-based organisation providing support and education around emotional and mental wellbeing.

Tel: 1890 474 474

Website: www.grow.ie

IACP (Counselling & Psychotherapy)

Irish Association for Counselling and Psychotherapy.

Tel: 01230 3536

Website: www.iacp.ie

Shine

Supporting people affected by mental ill-health.

Website: www.shine.ie

USA
Mental Health America (MHA)
The nation's leading community-based non-profit dedicated to addressing the needs of those living with mental illness and promoting the overall mental health of all Americans.

(800) 969-6642

Website: www.mentalhealthamerica.net

National Alliance on Mental Illness (NAMI)
NAMI provides advocacy, education, support and public awareness so that all individuals and families affected by mental illness can build better lives.

1-800-950-NAMI (6264)

Website: www.nami.org

ANXIETY / PANIC
Panic Disorder Information Hotline.

1-800-64-PANIC

Mental Health Crisis Lines / Suicide Hotlines
Suicide Prevention Lifeline.

1-800-273-TALK

Crisis Text Line
Crisis Text Line is the free, 24/7, confidential text message service for people in crisis.

Text HOME to 741741

CANADA

Crisis Services Canada

Providing suicide prevention and support to the people of Canada.

1-833-456-4566 or text 45645

Website: www.crisisservicescanada.ca

First Nations and Inuit Hope for Wellness Help Line

The Hope for Wellness Help Line offers immediate mental health counselling and crisis intervention to all Indigenous peoples across Canada.

1-855-242-3310

Website: www.hopeforwellness.ca

AUSTRALIA

Beyond Blue

Aims to increase awareness of depression and anxiety and reduce stigma.

Call 1300 22 4636, 24 hours / 7 days a week.

Website: www.beyondblue.org.au

eheadspace

Provides mental health and wellbeing support, information and services to young people aged 12 to 25 years and their families.

Call 1800 650 890, 9am-1am AEST / 7 days a week.

Website: www.headspace.org.au/eheadspace

Lifeline

Provides 24-hour crisis counselling, support groups and suicide prevention services.

Call 13 11 14.

Website: www.lifeline.org.au

MensLine Australia

A professional telephone and online support and information service for Australian men.

Call 1300 78 99 78, 24 hours / 7 days a week.

Website: www.mensline.org.au

MindSpot

A free telephone and online service for people with stress, worry, anxiety, low mood or depression. MindSpot is not an emergency or instant response service.

Call 1800 61 44 34 AEST, 8am-8pm (Mon-Fri), 8am-6pm (Sat).

Website: www.mindspot.org.au

PANDA (Perinatal Anxiety & Depression Australia)

Provides a national telephone information, counselling and referral service

Call 1300 726 306, 9am-7:30pm AEST (Mon-Fri).

Website: www.panda.org.au

SANE Australia

Provides support, training & education for those with a mental illness to lead a better life.

Call 1800 18 7263, 10am-10pm AEST (Mon-Fri).

Website: www.sane.org

Suicide Call Back Service

Provides 24/7 support if you or someone you know is feeling suicidal.

Call 1300 659 467.

Website: www.suicidecallbackservice.org.au

Open Arms

Veterans and Families Counselling provides 24/7 free and confidential, nationwide counselling and support for war and service-related mental health.

Call 1800 011 046.

Website: www.openarms.gov.au

NEW ZEALAND

National helplines

New Zealand's national mental health & addictions helpline number.

Need to talk? Free call or text 1737 any time for support from a trained counsellor.

Website: www.1737.org.nz

Lifeline

Lifeline Aotearoa's helpline and textline provides 24/7, confidential support from qualified counsellors and trained volunteers.

0800 543 354 (0800 LIFELINE) or free text 4357 (HELP)

Website: www.lifeline.org.nz

Samaritans

Samaritans offer confidential, non-religious and non-judgemental support to anyone who may be feeling depressed, lonely, or even be contemplating suicide.

0800 726 666

Website: www.samaritans.org.nz

Depression Helpline

Free 24/7 Helpline

0800 111 757 or free text 4202 (to talk to a trained counsellor about how you are feeling or to ask any questions).

www.depression.org.nz

Family Services 211 Helpline

For help finding (and direct transfer to) community-based health and social support services in your area.

0800 211 211

Skylight

For support through trauma, loss and grief.

0800 299 100, 9 am–5 pm weekdays.

Website: www.skylight.org.nz/get-support/counselling

Anxiety phone line

Free helpline giving vital support to hundreds of people each month who experience all forms of anxiety, including Panic Attacks, Phobias and Obsessive Compulsive Disorders.

0800 269 4389 (0800 ANXIETY)

Website: www.anxiety.org.nz

ACKNOWLEDGEMENTS

Writing this book around having a full-time job and being a hands-on father of two young children, one 2 and a half years old and the other 8 months old has been challenging. I have written it in the evenings for months and months, often tired but determined to see it through to the end. I am so pleased to have reached this section of the book as that means it is finished, and I can now share it with the world.

I have always had a passion for writing, and mental health is something that is extremely close to my heart. Having suffered from anxiety on and off since being a teenager, I wanted to write a book that I wish someone had handed to me at the start of my journey with it. I still have good days and bad days, like most people do, but what's important is that I accept my anxiety, I understand why I can feel the way I do sometimes, and I know how to manage it to make the most out of my life.

Life can be challenging for us all, but it can also be beautiful. I have learned throughout my life to be grateful for the things that are truly important, and that is my health, happiness, family and friends. Everything else is just a bonus.

With that said, the people I would like to acknowledge are my family and friends. Firstly, I would like to thank my beautiful wife Danielle for her constant support since the day we met, and for always believing in me. I would also like to thank her for her patience with me while writing this book and for being an amazing mum to my two beautiful children. To Oliver and Summer, my sunshine and light. I want to thank you for being my inspiration and strength, to be the best version of me I can be. You fill my life with laughter and make my heart full.

To my parents Kyla, Gerard and Anne. Thank you for your constant love and support and for always believing in me and filling me with confidence and self-belief. It means more than you'll ever know.

To my in-laws Christine and Neville. Thank you for your love and support also. We are blessed to have great parents on all sides. Thank you to Andrea for your love and support too.

To my Uncle Mark, thank you for inspiring me to write from a young age. The poetry and letters we shared growing up is something that I am grateful for and has stayed with me to this day.

To my sisters Chloe and Kelly. Thank you for always having my back no matter what. We have shared so much laughter over the years, and I know you are always there to turn to if I need you.

To my brother in law Dave, my nephews and Godson's Myles and Teddy, my Goddaughter Orla, Nanna Patsy, Pauline and Grandma Grace – you all mean the world to me.

Thank you to my wider family, the Jenkins, the Ryan's, the Burbeary's and the Massey's. I have so many amazing memories with you all, and they have all helped to shape the person I am, as I write this book today.

To my family and friends in heaven, including my Granny Mondinho, Nanna Eileen, Grandad Gerard and Aunty Debbie. I wish I would have got to spend more time with you than I did but life can be cruel and short. Thank you for the times we shared though and for the love you gave to me. I'll see you all one day but hopefully not too soon.

To my close friends, Sam, Ste, Paul Jones, Paul Giblin and Thian. We've had some amazing times over the years, and you have all enjoyed the rollercoaster with me. Long may it continue. To Paul McDonald, cheers for keeping the Scottish connections alive.

Thank you to Ryan Ridgway and Frankie Parker for reading through the book and providing your professional opinion, and to Ryan again for providing the foreword.

The final word goes to my Aunty Sharon and my Grandad Malcolm – a doctor of psychotherapy and counselling. Two amazing people who helped me to grow into the person I am today. They were caring, supportive, wise, witty, intelligent and beautiful people. You are two shining stars in my night sky, and I hope you enjoyed watching over me as I wrote this book.

THE END